SONGS OF THE IRISH

SONGS OF THE IRISH

An Anthology of

Irish Folk Music and Poetry with

English Verse Translations

compiled and edited by

DONAL O'SULLIVAN

DUBLIN

BROWNE & NOLAN LIMITED

First published 1960
by Browne & Nolan Limited
41-42 Nassau Street, Dublin
Printed in Great Britain
by Lowe & Brydone (Printers) Limited
London, N.W.10

To Bryan and Elisabeth

FOREWORD

I desire to acknowledge the kind permission given to me to use copyright material as follows, the respective sources being recorded in the Combined Index at the end of this volume (p. 192):

in respect of tunes or texts (and in a few cases of both tunes and texts), to Messrs. A. Martin Freeman, Fionán Mac Coluim, Cormac Ó Cadhla and Pádraig Ó Siocfhradha; to the late Tadhg Ó Donnchadha, Risteárd Ó Foghludha and T. F. O'Rahilly; and to the literary executors of the Rev. P. A. Walsh, C.M.

in respect of translations, to Mr. Freeman and the late Dr. Douglas Hyde; Mr. Dermot F. Fahy, owner of the copyright in the published verse of his father, the late Francis A. Fahy; Mr. Donagh MacDonagh, owner of the copyright in the published verse of his father, the late Thomas MacDonagh; and Mr. Donn S. Piatt and Mrs. Emmet Humphreys, who jointly own the copyright in the works of their grandfather, the late Dr. George Sigerson.

Questions of copyright apart, I have given in the List of Sources the collectors of the songs and also, so far as possible, the names of the persons from whom they were obtained, as well as the places in which they lived.

A few of my verse translations have already appeared in the *Irish Times*, the *Journal of the Royal Society of Antiquaries of Ireland* and a pamphlet entitled *Irish Folk Music and Song* issued by the Cultural Relations Committee of Ireland. Permission to republish is hereby acknowledged.

My cordial thanks are due to an anonymous patron of the arts and to the Arts Council of Ireland for grants in aid which have made publication possible.

I am deeply grateful for the good counsel given to me on matters musical and linguistic by Professor Aloys Fleischmann and the late Professor Gerard Murphy respectively. I also wish to thank Mr. Seán Jennett, who read the work in proof and gave me the benefit of his expert knowledge of typography; Miss Veronica Kennedy, who read all the proofs over with me and made an independent check of the music; and Mr. Seán Ó Súilleabháin, Archivist of the Irish Folklore Commission, who read my typescript and placed at my service his wide acquaintance with the spoken Irish language.

DONAL O'SULLIVAN

Dublin

CONTENTS

SONGS OF THE HARPERS

INTRODUCTION

Nearly thirty years ago my friend the late Alfred Perceval Graves published his *Celtic Song Book*, consisting of representative popular songs from Ireland, Scotland, Wales, Britanny and the Isle of Man. The Scots Gaelic, Welsh, Breton and Manx originals were given, with verse translations; but so far as Ireland was concerned "no Gaelic words had been found worthy to mate the Irish melodies Moore and other Anglo-Irish lyrists had helped to immortalise." Hence, "the Irish language being lyrically derelict for his purpose", Mr. Graves was compelled to fall back upon the familiar nineteenth century songs in English by Moore, Lover, Davis, Lady Dufferin and others. Without disparagement to the memory of the genial author of "Father O'Flynn" (who was unacquainted with Irish), it must be said that these statements are completely unfounded; but the fact that they could be confidently made by a man of his standing is evidence of the general lack of knowledge on this subject. To do something to remedy that lack is the purpose of this book.

So far from being "lyrically derelict", the Irish language is in truth a treasure-house of song, and its folk-poetry is among the most abundant of any country in Europe. The beauty of Irish music has long been universally recognized; the equal beauty of the verse to which that music was sung has been accorded no such recognition. Moreover, apart from the pleasure of aesthetic appreciation anyone who wishes to understand the mind and soul of the Irish people must have recourse to their songs—if not in the original at least in such faithful translations as are available to him. He will scarcely make his discoveries through such pieces as "The Harp That Once Through Tara's Halls", "The Whistlin' Thief", "The West's Asleep" or "Dublin Bay".

As to the general plan of the present anthology: my object being to cover the entire field of Irish folk-song in Irish, I decided upon fifteen categories, ranging from Lullabies to Songs of the Harpers, which taken together might fairly be regarded as comprehensive. Out of the very many hundreds of our songs, I then allotted to each category a selection sufficient to make it representative of the subject with which it deals. All the tunes are authentic Irish folk melodies, though in most cases they were noted independently of the words, since the collectors of the tunes did not know Irish and the collectors of the verse did not know music. But the title of the tune (even when wrongly spelt or mistranslated) provides a clue to the appropriate words; and with two unavoidable exceptions the songs are here united to tunes to which they were traditionally sung by the people.

The book being designed for the general reader, it was necessary to provide verse translations in the original metre. The choice of songs had been made without regard to whether such translations existed, and it was found that less than one third had been rendered into English verse. Hence it fell to me to translate the remainder. The task, whether well done or ill done, was not so arduous as it might seem; for, knowing the originals for the most part by heart and having the tunes in my head, I found that all but the longest took shape readily enough during my country walks and merely needed to be committed to paper. Many of the Irish poems attain a high degree of poetic excellence; with these I was obviously unable to do more than provide a metrical substitute which would be singable and convey the meaning as nearly as may be. Others, less intractable, demanded only that their native simplicity should not be marred or misrepresented. A few—very few—hardly rise above the level of the broadsheet ballad, and a more pretentious treatment than that accorded them would have been out of place. In short, my humble purpose has been to exhibit the metrical structure in each case, to convey something of the spirit, and to render the meaning in so far as to do so is compatible with the difference in idiom of the two languages and with the exigencies of rhyme.

To supplement these renderings (whether by myself or another) I have prepared in every instance a translation into English prose, by which the reader may correct the freedom of the verse. Here I have tried to avoid being slavishly literal, while at the same time burking none of the textual difficulties that occasionally present themselves, difficulties inevitable in the case of verse that has been handed down traditionally. It is hoped that, with the tune before him, the verse rendering and the prose translation, anyone who may wish to study the manners and customs of the Irish people through the medium of their songs will not find himself too greatly handicapped by a lack of knowledge of their language.

For the purpose of the music the Irish has been treated as the primary text, the method of singing the English version being indicated in the usual manner by the insertion of alternative notes, as requisite. There being no accepted standard of Irish spelling, I have felt free to adopt shorter forms than those in common use when to do so would give a clearer indication of the pronunciation, e.g., *túirt* for *tabhairt* (giving) and *oíche* for *oidhche* (night); but when the longer form is (or may be) indicative of a dialectical pronunciation I have let it stand. Also, when a short vowel sound between two consonants is not normally represented in the spelling it has been necessary to insert it for singing purposes. Thus the word for "brave", *calma*, is pronounced *calama* and is therefore so spelt where it occurs under the music. (There is an English analogy in the word "helm", which was called "hellum" by old-time seamen in the days of sail.) Elision, which is a characteristic feature of Irish prosody, has been carried out in the verse placed under the music but not with the same strictness in the text, where it would probably serve merely as a distraction to the general reader.

Each of the fifteen sections into which the book is divided has been provided with a brief prefatory note of a general nature. For the rest, I have preferred to let the individual songs speak for themselves wherever possible, a note being appended only when there is something to be explained.

And now, what of the people here faithfully portrayed in the songs that they made and loved? What is the genesis of the songs themselves? How do both come to differ so markedly from the concepts of Ireland held by the world at large, and sometimes even by its own inhabitants? Answers to such questions demand a short historical sketch.

Anciently, Ireland was known as *insula doctorum et sanctorum*, the island of scholars and saints. We are not here concerned with the latter, but during the period of some centuries when the Gaelic civilization flourished it is probably not too much to say that the poet was

2

primarily a scholar. He received a prolonged training in the bardic schools, and he wrote highly stylized verse in classical metres according to strict and complex rules. His poems were intended for recitation before the chieftains and nobles who were his patrons, to a harp accompaniment, and he employed a vocabulary that would not have been "understanded of the people". Most important point of all, his poetry could not have been sung to any of the Irish airs that have come down to us. One cannot in general assign dates to our melodies, but any of them that existed at this epoch must have been the vehicle for poetry of an entirely different kind: popular poetry, employing vowel assonance. It is certain that such poetry existed alongside the other, unnoticed or despised by the scholar-poets and therefore not finding its way into the manuscripts of the time.

In the Preface to his *Lays of Ancient Rome*, Macaulay argues that for centuries prior to the Augustan Age there had existed a body of popular Latin poetry which owed nothing to the metres borrowed by the classical poets from Greece; and that this poetry, being sub-literary, became totally lost. If so, the parallel is fairly exact, except that in Ireland the popular poetry subsequently came to the surface in circumstances that will be described in a moment. A few of the songs in the present collection may conceivably date back to the period when it was more or less submerged: "The Small Black Rose", for instance, and perhaps one or two of the lullabies and love-songs. But there are two other cases in which it is possible to be more precise.

The oldest Irish airs preserved in manuscript are the few contained in the Fitzwilliam Virginal Book, which dates from about the year 1620 and is in the Fitzwilliam Museum at Cambridge. One of these (p. 277) is entitled "Callino Casturame". This is undoubtedly Pistol's "Calen o custure me" in Shakespeare's *Henry V* (iv, 4), as correctly amended by Malone: and Professor Gerard Murphy has shown* that this is a phonetic representation of the title of a popular song in assonantal metre (otherwise lost) which is quoted by a learned poet of not later than the early seventeenth century: "*Cailín ó chois tSiúire me*", meaning "I am a girl from beside the [river] Suir". (If it be thought odd that such a phrase could occur in Shakespeare, it may be mentioned that in Ben Jonson's *New Inn* the disguised Lady Frampul replies when asked what she will take to drink, "Er grac Chreest tower een cuppaw[n] d'usquebagh doone!", which is good phonetic Irish for "For the love of Christ give us a cup of whiskey!")

Another such song is "*Thugamar féin an samhra linn*" ("We brought the summer with us"), which, being associated with pastoral May Day ceremonies, is doubtless of consider-able antiquity. Though the earliest version of the tune does not appear till 1745, reliable tradition says that the song was sung as a welcome to the Duke of Ormonde when he landed as Lord Lieutenant after the Restoration (July, 1662). Versions of the words have survived in the Irish-speaking districts until the present day, and one of the last of the learned poets, David Ó Bruadair (c. 1625–1697), alludes to the song twice in one of his poems. This poet contemptuously refers to assonantal verse as *sráid-éigse* ("street poetry"), and writing some time after 1692 he bitterly complains that "nothing but vulgar poetry is now understood".†

Perhaps a word might be here interpolated regarding the age of our Irish melodies.

*Éigse, I, 125.

†MacErlean's edition, II, 34 and III, 194.

3

Bunting, the earliest of the systematic collectors, called his published volumes *Ancient Music of Ireland*, and two of his successors, Petrie and Joyce, followed his example by incorporating the word "Ancient" in their titles. The term is of course a vague one, but the idea has certainly got abroad that there is something especially antique and venerable about Irish traditional tunes as compared with those of other nations. I know of no good grounds for supposing this to be so. It is true that the harp is of extreme antiquity in Ireland, and that as early as the twelfth century the musical qualities of its people were the subject of favourable comment by Giraldus Cambrensis and others. These, however, are generalities, and one cannot assign a date to a particular melody merely by inspecting it, and without extrinsic evidence. Moreover, any folk-tune, until it is crystallized by being reduced to writing, is constantly being subjected to a process of modification and change at the hands of the folk. To suggest that some few of our extant airs may possibly date back for some centuries is one thing; but to hold that the general body of Irish folk-music is peculiarly deserving of the term "ancient" is quite another.

The old Gaelic civilization was unable to withstand indefinitely the incessant assaults made upon it by the English, and the Cromwellian Settlement in the middle of the seventeenth century may be said to have brought about its final collapse. The bardic schools ceased to exist and with them the type of verse that, cramped with rules and swathed in technicalities as it was, was yet the only kind that had till then been deemed worthy of serious notice. The Irish poetical spirit burst its bonds, and assonantal poetry came into its own. It became the medium alike of the unknown composers of our folk-songs and of the learned poets who were the successors of the bards; and it is true lyrical poetry, intended to be sung. It is in fact the medium of all the songs included in the present collection.

To convey a clear idea of the structure of this assonantal verse is not easy, since the genius of Irish prosody differs so greatly from that of English. Briefly, it consists of an arrangement of repetitions of the same vowel sounds, cunningly placed so that almost every stressed syllable in a line forms part of the assonantal pattern. From the musical standpoint these assonances fall on the beat and in some cases on the half-beat as well. Even in the humble folk-poetry the effect is mellifluous and pleasing; but in the hands of a master the rich flowing rhythms, varied harmonies and untroubled ease of echo and reminiscence are something to marvel at, the result being the kind of poetry that is not merely made for music but is in some sort music itself. To take "The Mower" as an example (p. 134), the opening three lines have each three assonances (é, ú, ă), these being repeated in the same order in lines 5–7 and again in lines 11–13. Lines 4, 8 and 14, rounding off the several quatrains, have two each (é, á); and the long middle lines which correspond to the turn of the melody (lines 9 and 10) have four each (ŏ, ŏ, é, á). This gives no less than 41 assonances to a single verse, and a total of 287 in a comparatively short poem of seven stanzas. Here is a deftness that amounts to genius, for it not only produces a song abounding in harmonies but, employing none save poetic words, achieves a lyric instinct with poetic feeling. And yet the eighteenth century poets in Munster and South Ulster wrote such songs by the score, in different metres to suit a wide variety of popular airs; and, like the songs of Robert Burns in Scotland, the people took them to their hearts and sang them in the same way as they did their folk melodies.

4

When the two languages first confronted each other in Ireland, the native speech more than held its own for a short period—say from 1300 to 1550. But during the centuries thereafter English has been ousting Irish as a spoken tongue. When the tide recedes from a rocky foreshore it does not ebb evenly but leaves pools of varying size, which gradually grow smaller until they finally disappear. This is very much what has happened and is still happening to Irish—except that there can hardly be a return of the tide. During most of the eighteenth century it is likely that Irish was still the dominant language, apart from the towns and the Pale; but the position gradually worsened, the "pools" becoming ever smaller. By the turn of the century the masters of assonantal verse had virtually disappeared. Their successors, such as Anthony Raftery in Mayo and Tomás Rua Ó Súilleabháin in Kerry, were few in number and lacked both their scholarship and their inspiration. The Great Famine of the middle of the last century was as catastrophic from the linguistic aspect as from all others, turning a slow process of change into a swift metamorphosis. Since then, bad systems of education, economic factors and general apathy have combined still further to contract the areas in which Irish is still spoken, so that at the present time it is indigenous only to certain localities in our coastal counties and the adjacent islands. Even so, the practice of folk-song remains surprisingly vigorous in such places, as the recent researches of the Irish Folk Lore Commission have shown; and the making of new verse by local rhymers is not unknown.

We now turn to our popular songs in English, and here we come across an astonishing contrast. They differ enormously from their Irish counterparts, and the difference is indicative of the profound effect of the loss of their language on the psychology and character of the Irish people. Of course English had been for a prolonged period the language of many of the towns, and Limerick had its "Garryowen", Mallow its "Rakes of Mallow", Derry its "No Surrender", and so on: popular songs in English sung to characteristic Irish airs. Dublin, never a Gaelic-speaking city, had a number of racy songs peculiar to itself, such as "The Night Before Larry Was Stretched", "Cockles and Mussels", "The Kilmainham Minuet" and "Finnegan's Wake"—from which last James Joyce presumably got the title for the successor to *Ulysses*. As to the countryside, there can be no doubt that the many thousands of English and Scots who obtained lands in Ireland during the seventeenth century brought their folk-songs with them: the planters under James I, the Cromwellian soldiery, the victors in the Williamite War. Versions of purely English and Scottish folk-songs are common enough in Ireland, and they could hardly have got here in such large numbers in any other way. At the time of Oliver Goldsmith's childhood (about 1740) his native county of Longford was almost entirely Irish-speaking; but the poet was of English stock, his home atmosphere was English, and the songs he remembered being sung to him by his nurse were "Johnny Armstrong's Last Good-Night" and "Barbara Allan". Naturally enough, the Irish learnt and sang such English songs in course of time, but we are not here so much concerned with them as with the ones the Irish made for themselves, and the transition from the eighteenth to the nineteenth century provides a convenient starting-point.

Patriotic poetry is not wholly absent from Irish Gaelic literature; but while the country remained Irish-speaking the recurrent risings against English rule produced few songs of a

5

kind to stir the blood, as patriotic songs should do. The insurrections of 1798 and 1803 showed a marked change, and a whole crop of genuine folk-songs dates from this period, including "The Boys of Wexford", "Bold Robert Emmet", "The Shan Van Vocht", "Billy Byrne of Ballymanus" and "The Croppy Boy". "The Wearing of the Green" also appeared about this time, though the form in which it has become famous represents a re-writing of the old words by Dion Boucicault. Incidentally, the tune is of Lowland Scottish origin. All the songs just mentioned were printed on broadsheets, which in the early part of the nineteenth century became as familiar a feature of the countryside as they had previously been in the towns, being eagerly bought up at markets and fairs and other places where the people congregated.

These broadsheets dealt with a wide variety of themes: local disasters; elopements; the departure of emigrants; purported confessions of men awaiting execution for murder; skits on the new police, like "The Peeler and the Goat"; prize-fights such as the one fought by Donnelly and Cooper, and later, Heenan and Sayers; love songs; in fact, anything and everything that by reason of its humour, pathos or general interest would be likely to appeal to the popular fancy. Few of them bore the slightest resemblance to the Gaelic songs which they had supplanted, and indeed they might have emanated from a nation poles apart from the one which created the songs gathered together in this book.

Upon occasion, however, a popular Gaelic folk-song was translated, and I give an instance of this in "The Little Bunch of Rushes" (p. 66). As often happened in such cases, the author, knowing English very imperfectly but with an ear accustomed to Irish prosody, unconsciously imitates the Gaelic assonance of the original. An even more striking example is afforded by a peasant song in praise of Castlehyde, on the Blackwater in County Cork. This contains the remarkable lines:

> The sweet improvements they would amuse you,
>   The trees are drooping with fruit all kind,
> The bees perfuming the fields with music,
>   Which yields more beauty to Castlehyde.

It will be seen that this quatrain is built up on the assonances í, ú (ee, oo); and though, like the rest of the song, it is doggerel, it is at least doggerel with a difference.

The song of "Castlehyde" is of interest in another connection, for it was in imitation of it that the Cork poet Richard Milliken wrote his caricature "The Groves of Blarney" and a second piece of the same general type, "The Groves of Blackpool" or "De Groves of de Pool". These began the vogue of the jocular, stage Irishman type of ditty which plagued Ireland for most of the nineteenth century, and it is a strange commentary on the mentality of the time that they achieved a high degree of popularity. Indeed, to judge by the cheap Irish song-books in circulation in New York, they still retain the esteem of Irish-Americans. In case the reader is unfamiliar with such, here are the first verse and chorus of one of the best-known, "Barney Brallaghan's Courtship":

> 'Twas on a windy night,
>   At two o'clock in the morning,
> An Irish lad so tight,
>   All wind and weather scorning,

At Judy Callaghan's door,
    Sitting on the palings,
His love he did deplore,
    And this was part of his wailings:
        'Only say
    You'll have Mister Brallaghan,
        Don't say nay,
    Charming Judy Callaghan!'

Of course it must be said that such productions owed their popularity in great part to the fact that they were written to native tunes (mostly dance tunes) that were at once lively and attractive. Here is a specimen of somewhat later vintage:

In the town of Athy one Jeremy Lannigan
    Battered away till he hadn't a pound;
His father he died and made him a man again,
    Left him a house and ten acres of ground.
He gave a grand party to friends and relations
    Who did not forget him when sent to the wall;
If you'll only listen I'll make your eyes glisten
    At the rows and the ructions at Lannigan's Ball.

It is surprising that people whose immediate forbears had enjoyed the riches of Gaelic poetry could stomach this type of verse, even though much of it is good fun; but it is still more surprising that they should have been so completely captivated by Tom Moore. Moore was accounted one of the greatest poets of his age (Heine placed him on the same level as Byron); but he wrote primarily for a cultured, if not sophisticated, public in the English tradition. Yet from the publication of the First Number in 1807 right up to the time of the Parnell Movement and beyond it is not too much to say that Moore's *Irish Melodies* formed the secular hymn-book of Irish nationalism. One might have expected that his patriotic songs would have made an appeal: pieces like "Rich and Rare", "The Minstrel Boy" and "She is Far from the Land". But the public acclaim extended to virtually the whole of the *Melodies*, including songs like "Believe me, if all those endearing young charms" and "Love's Young Dream", which have no obvious connection with Ireland. The tunes used by Moore were mostly genuine traditional melodies of his native country, and his lyrics matched them with a skill hardly approached before or since. The Irish people were fortunate in finding a poet of his genius to cheer and divert them "in dark and evil days".

The change in national psychology produced by the change of language has already been touched upon. In this connection it is of interest to note that Moore's *Melodies* were translated into Irish by John McHale, Archbishop of Tuam. Moore wrote to McHale (and the sentiment does him great credit), "Your Irish (truly Irish) Melodies are a shame and a reproach to me, and I would willingly give up what I know of other languages to have been Irishman enough to accomplish such a work." Yet these translations were a failure in the Irish-speaking districts, and even if they had been more competently done the result would have been no different. The truth is that the themes are completely alien in spirit from the Gaelic tradition.

Samuel Lover, who was a contemporary of Moore's, was a connoisseur of Irish music and also used Irish tunes (though by no means exclusively) for his songs. Though not to be compared with Moore as a poet, he wrote out of a rather more intimate knowledge of the Ireland of his time: and if some of his pieces, such as "The Low-backed Car", "I'm

Not Myself At All" and "The Whistlin' Thief", seem to us to smack of Donnybrook Fair, there are others which evince a considerable depth of poetic feeling: "What Will You Do, Love?", for instance, and "Oh! Native Music", and "A Baby Was Sleeping". All alike were indiscriminately received by the populace.

An event of the most profound significance in Irish history was the rise of the Young Ireland movement in the early forties of the last century and the foundation of its newspaper, *The Nation*, of which the first number appeared on the 15th October, 1842. No praise could be too high for the ideals of the band of devoted men and women gathered together under its aegis, but we are here concerned solely with the results of the movement on the songs of the people. The motto of the paper was "To create and foster public opinion in Ireland and make it racy of the soil"; and Thomas Davis made an impassioned appeal to his fellow-countrymen to provide a minstrelsy conformable with these ideals. "If they be men generous in friendship, hearty at the hearth, tranced by sweet or maddened by strong sounds, sobbing with unused strength and fiery for freedom and glory, then they can write lyrics for every class in Ireland."

Would that this were true! But the wind of poetry bloweth where it listeth, and it ill consorts with propaganda—even propaganda of the most righteous and high-minded kind. Moreover, the soil was infertile for the reception of genuine poetry in English. About half the population west of a line drawn from Waterford to Derry still spoke Irish habitually, and through many decades of misgovernment the English-speaking peasantry were still to a large extent illiterate. The difficulties were therefore enormous, and added to them was the fact that to write of set purpose verse that will capture the popular emotion is a thing impossible. One of the poetesses of *The Nation*, Ellen Mary Downing, wrote that she "would rather write one little song that a child or peasant might sing and feel than a very miracle-poem of abstraction and profundity". It is more easily said than done.

Nevertheless, a very gallant effort was made, and during the brief existence of *The Nation* it printed a good deal of verse of a high standard with the appropriate melodies, of which some were traditional and others specially composed. Davis gathered round him a notable group of writers—M. J. Barry, D'Arcy McGee, Lady Wilde, John O'Hagan, Eva Mary Kelly, Denis Florence McCarthy, to mention only a few. Their unflagging purpose was to awaken in the Irish race a vivid sense of what was great and noble in its past; and they have undoubtedly given to Anglo-Irish literature much that is valuable and enduring. Maybe they were trying the Irish people too high in the circumstances of the time; maybe the Irish are not so responsive to the patriotic emotion as is generally supposed, in this respect resembling their Gaelic-speaking ancestors. Whatever the cause, the poets of *The Nation* failed to capture the farmsteads and the cabins except in their simplest and most artless pieces such as Davis's "Annie Dear": though they naturally met with better success in the towns. Of their patriotic songs, comparatively few achieved a degree of popularity. McCann's "O'Donnell Aboo" is one of these, others being Denny Lane's "Carrigdhown" and Davis's "The West's Asleep"; but all were outstripped by "The Memory of the Dead", written by Ingram and composed by Hudson—and this fine song is English rather than Irish in sentiment. In 1846 the songs were published with the music in a single volume, entitled *The Spirit of the Nation*; but this remained virtually a dead book, whereas collected editions of Moore's *Irish Melodies* continued to sell by the thousand, in some cases as cheaply as a shilling a copy. The next movement of national resurgence, that of the Fenians in the sixties, attempted no such literary renaissance but was concerned purely with physical force. Yet it produced at least two patriotic songs that were being sung before long throughout the length and breadth of the land: Kickham's "Patrick Sheehan" and Casey's "Rising of the Moon".

Contemporary with these two men was a writer of a very different type, whose songs were no less popular than theirs. This was Lady Dufferin, a grand-daughter of Sheridan the dramatist. The feeling which inspired her "Irish Emigrant" ("I'm Sitting on the Stile, Mary") was perhaps a less vicarious emotion than that which gave rise to an equally celebrated song by her sister, the Honourable Mrs. Norton, "The Arab's Farewell to His Steed"; yet in her other songs one feels that in essentials she is as far removed from Ireland as from Araby. In "Dublin Bay", for example, with its sentimental references to "the cabin" and "the childher", and its atrocious opening rhymes:

> O Bay of Dublin! my heart you're troublin',
> Your beauty haunts me like a fevered dream;
> Like frozen fountains that the sun sets bubblin',
> My heart's blood warms when I but hear your name.

And yet this was no less popular with the Irish people than her "Katey's Letter" with its forced jocularity, which—not to speak too harshly—might have been intended for mental defectives:

> Och! girls, and did you ever hear
> I wrote my love a letter,
> And although he cannot read
> Sure I thought it all the better.
> For why should he be puzzled
> By hard spelling in the matter,
> When the meaning was so plain,
> That I love him faithfully?
> *I love him faithfully,*
> *And he knows it, oh! he knows it,*
> *Without one word from me!*

The sentimental drawing-room ballad (a class to which such songs belong) arose in the middle of the Victorian era, and it had a vogue which is hardly yet exhausted. Readers of *John Bull's Other Island* may recall that when Nora Reilly is seated by the Round Tower in the moonlight, waiting for her lover, she hums "not an Irish melody but a hackneyed English drawing-room ballad of the season before last"; and this is no mere Shavian paradox. Ireland and the Irish were the theme of many such pieces, though they were seldom by Irish writers or set to native tunes. In addition to Lady Dufferin's songs, one might mention Balfe's "Killarney" and Molloy's "Oh! the Days of the Kerry Dancing"; and Weatherly, an English composer, chose for his "Danny Boy"—unfortunately, as we may think—one of the loveliest of all Irish melodies, the so-called "Londonderry Air" noted by Miss Jane Ross in Limavady and published as a tune without title by Petrie in 1855. Apart from a few nostalgic pieces like "Come Back to Erin" and "Oh! Barney, take Me Home Again", these "Irish" drawing-room ballads were mostly love-songs, in which the lack of the authentic note in either music or words was met by the adoption of an Irish place-name in the title— "The Rose of Tralee" is an example—or by a plentiful distribution in the text of acushlas, colleens, machrees, alannahs and mavourneens:

9

Soon I'll be back to the colleen I adore,
Eileen alannah oggus asthore!

No wonder that Charles Stanford wrote in one of his letters to A. P. Graves, "The public is bored to death with overdone *patois* Irish!"

These two Irishmen—the one a musician of high distinction, the other a graceful and facile writer of lyrics—joined forces in an endeavour to provide something better. Stanford had been entrusted by Petrie's daughter with the publication of her father's musical manuscripts, containing about two thousand airs; so here at any rate was a vast body of authentic Irish melodies from which to choose. The selection was made with care and discrimination, and the collaboration, beginning with *Songs of Ireland* in 1882, continued for more than twenty years. Stanford's arrangements are all that could be desired from the musician's standpoint, and Graves showed much ability and industry as a song-writer on native themes in diverse metres. The result is a collection of genuine Irish *art* songs, justly popular on the concert platform, not a few of which are likely to endure. Graves, however, persisted till the day of his death in regarding his work and Stanford's as a substantial contribution to Irish *folk* song, which in the nature of things it could not be. In conversation with him I once delicately suggested something of the sort, but his pained surprise was obviously so genuine that I did not pursue the matter. He lacked the common touch so abundantly possessed by his contemporaries Francis A. Fahy and P. J. McCall, but these had no collaborator on the musical side and they are now hardly remembered save by one song apiece—"The Ould Plaid Shawl" and "Kelly, the Boy from Killann". Indeed, modern Ireland has given its heart to a writer of a very different type, the late Percy French, whose songs are in the tradition of Milliken and Lover: "Phil the Fluter's Ball", "The Mountains of Mourne" (written to the same air as Lane's "Carrigdhown"), "Come Back, Paddy Reilly, to Ballyjamesduff", and so on.

The National Literary Society was founded in 1891 and the Gaelic League two years later, the name of William Butler Yeats being imperishably associated with the former and that of Douglas Hyde with the latter. An outline of the development of Irish popular song is not the place to dwell at any length on the profoundly revitalizing effects on the national life and culture of the twin movements thus initiated, but both have repercussions on our subject. The one sought to give Ireland a literature which, albeit in the English language, would be quick with a life that might in time be felt by the entire nation, irrespective of religion or politics—a literature which would largely draw its inspiration from the well-springs of the nation's Gaelic past. The aim of the other was to preserve and to propagate the spoken Irish language and to raise it from the level of a despised vernacular to that of the noble medium of speech and of letters which is its due.

Unlike the Young Irelanders (whose aim was political), the protagonists of the literary renaissance were not specially concerned with song-writing, their genius finding its expression for the most part in drama, in imaginative prose and in poetry not intended for music. One of Yeats's loveliest lyrics, "Down by the Salley Gardens", was written when he was a boy down in Sligo and was set by Graves to an appropriate Irish folk tune. But it remains a solitary example, as the appeal of our old traditional songs formed no essential part of his nature. Later poets, however, essayed with some success to re-model a few of them, as

Burns did for Scotland: as, for instance Pádraic Colum in "She Moved Through the Fair" and Joseph Campbell in "The Ninepenny Fidil". These are among the many songs charmingly arranged to native melodies by the late Herbert Hughes—a task in which he deserved well of his country.

Two of Yeats's earliest prose works, *The Celtic Twilight* and *The Secret Rose*, are permeated with that spirit of mystery and dream which is sometimes loosely described as mysticism—though the term used for St. Teresa and St. John of the Cross seems of doubtful applicability. However that may be, the influence of these books has been such as to create the widespread belief that the genius of Gaelic Ireland possesses some peculiarly occult or esoteric quality. Indeed, the very term "Celtic twilight" is now commonly accepted as expressive of this supposed characteristic, though it is sometimes humorously referred to as "the mist that does be on the bog", from a phrase in Synge's *Shadow of the Glen*. It must here be stated categorically that a survey of Gaelic literature as a whole discloses no ground whatever for such a belief; and to state the fact implies no blindness to the exceeding beauty of such lines as:

> The host is riding from Knocknarea
> And over the grave of Clooth-na-bare;
> Caoilte tossing his burning hair
> And Niamh calling away, come away:
> Empty your heart of its mortal dream.

This is high poetry. We may well be glad and proud that it was an Irishman who wrote it so long as we do not fall into the error of supposing that it derives even remotely from the Gaelic past, in which Caoilte and Niamh are as substantial and unethereal as the Hector and Helen of Homer. Yeats's genius is *sui generis;* but his symbolism and "Celtic" dreaming owe something, no doubt, to the writings of Ernest Renan and Matthew Arnold, something to the Rosicrucians, something to theosophy. They owe nothing to anything he may have heard from the country people when he was a boy down in Sligo.

The point is of relevance here because if the spirit of mysticism existed it would assuredly manifest itself in the songs of the people. The present collection is fully representative of those songs over a period of centuries, yet they disclose no hint of such a spirit. It is true that some writers have professed to find it, but they were unconsciously under Yeats's influence and they were seeing what is not there. P. H. Pearse classes "Éamonn an Chnuic" and "Druimfhionn Donn Dílis" as "examples of the mystical patriotic songs of the later Irish". He states that he "cannot entirely fathom" the former, nor does he "think anyone can fathom it"; and he expresses the opinion that "the 'Druimfhionn Donn' is the most beautiful of the Irish mystical songs, and the strangest except perhaps 'The Yellow Bittern', which who understands?" The three songs named are all included in this book (pp. 124, 143, 150), and I leave others to judge of the degree of mysticism (if any) shown by the first two. As to "The Yellow Bittern", this is a straightforward, if somewhat whimsical, song on the subject of drink.

The seed planted by the pioneers of the Irish language movement germinated more slowly. Still, it would be a mistake, I think, unduly to

> contrast
> The petty done, the undone vast.

11

It is true that the decay of Irish in the districts where it is indigenous has hardly been arrested; but it now seems likely that the original hopes were set too high and that Ireland must be content with something less. If we cannot "call back yesterday, bid time return", at least we can say that for some while longer this beautiful and mellifluous tongue will remain as the everyday speech of many of our glens and in remote places by the sea; and that, given the taste and a modicum of skill, we can readily learn to speak it ourselves. On this credit side, it may be affirmed with certainty that the number of people who can read and enjoy Irish Gaelic literature has multiplied out of all recognition since 1893, and that this process is likely to continue. The riches of Irish poetry and prose have been made available to them by an honourable succession of scholars, and there are of gifted contemporary writers not a few. The songs in this book are no "museum pieces"; there is a public capable of reading them and singing them with pleasure. There is also, it may be, a wider public which, by perusing these Songs of the Irish, may care to make the better acquaintance of a people whose true nature is often ill-known or misunderstood. The compiler salutes all alike as he ceases to interpose himself between the reader and these melodies.

LULLABIES

In the old Ireland, sleep-music (*suantraí*) was reckoned as one of the principal categories of song, the others being lively music (*geantraí*) and sorrowful music (*goltraí*). Hence it is not surprising that we number among our Irish melodies an abundance of nurse-tunes, many of which are of singular beauty. But the appropriate words, where they exist at all, are too often found in mere fugitive and fragmentary snatches of no special value.

Of the complete lullabies, the four here included may be taken to be fairly representative of the class as a whole, as regards both the music and the words.

DEIRÍN DÉ   DERREEN DAY

Deirín dé, deirín dé,
Tá'n gabhairín oíche amuh san bhfraoch,
Deirín dé, deirín dé,
Tá'n bunán donn a' labhairt san bhféith.

Deirín dé, deirín dé,
Geóidh ba siar le h-éirghe an lae,
Deirín dé, deirín dé,
Is raghaidh mo leanbh 'á bhfeighilt ar féar.

Deirín dé, deirín dé,
Eireóidh gealach is raghaidh grian fé,
Deirín dé, deirín dé,
Tiocfaidh ba aniar le deire an lae.

Deirín dé, deirín dé,
Leogfad mo leanbh a' pioca sméar,
Deirín dé, deirín dé,
—Ach codail go sámh go fáinne an lae!

Derreen day, derreen day,
The nightjar calls upon the heath,
Derreen day, derreen day,
The bittern booms the reeds beneath.

Derreen day, derreen day,
Cows will go west at dawn of day,
Derreen day, derreen day,
My darling will watch them lest they stray.

Derreen day, derreen day,
The new moon greets the setting sun's ray,
Derreen day, derreen day,
Homeward the cows will wend their way.

Derreen day, derreen day,
I'll let my darling go gathering may,
Derreen day, derreen day,
If he sleeps soundly till dawn of day.

DONAL O'SULLIVAN

1. The nightjar is abroad in the heather, The brown bittern speaks in the reeds.
2. Cows will go west at dawn of day, And my child will go to mind them in the pasture.
3. The moon will rise and the sun will set, Cows will return at close of day.
4. I shall let my child go picking blackberries—But sleep soundly till daybreak !

15

Chuaidh mé go tigh na banaltra
  Le tuitim ceó na h-oíche,
'S ní raibh do chaoimhtheach leap' aici
  Ach a leanbh bán a' caoine.
D'fhiafraigh mé don bhanaltra
  Goidé 'bheir 'on leanbh síorghul;
'Sé dúirt sí go mba faisean dó
  Bheith a' crónán ins an oíche.

    Codla le n-a bhoga dhó,
      'Sé 'ní mo leanbh aimhréidh,
    Is codla le n-a bhoga dhó,
      'Sé 'ní mo leanbh aimhréidh!

Ní mar sin dom leanbh-sa,
  Do ré néall a chodlas sé,
Is mar bpóga daidí a bhanaltra
  Beidh a' leanbh aimhréidh.
Codla le n-a bhoga dhó,
  'Sé 'ní mo leanbh aimhréidh,
Is codla le n-a bhoga dhó,
  'Sé 'ní mo leanbh aimhréidh!

The mother stood beside her gate,
  On the fields the dew was lying,
No company had she so late
  But her little baby crying.
I asked, " What ails the little one?
  Why is he always fretting? "
She answered, " When the night draws on
  He cries for want of petting."

    He's sleeping while I'm rocking him,
      That's my fretful baby!
    Sleeping while I'm rocking him,
      That's my fretful baby!

My darling doesn't sleep a wink—
  Maybe I'm forgetful!
If daddy stays from home I think
  Baby will be fretful.
He's sleeping while I'm rocking him,
  That's my fretful baby!
Sleeping while I'm rocking him,
  That's my fretful baby!

Is maith an fear i mbaile mé,
　Níl dúil agam i mbíodán,
Is maith an fear i mbaile mé,
　Níl dúil agam i gcríochán.
Nuair éiríos fir a' bhaile amach
　A' breathnamh ar a ndíobháil,
Fillim ar a' mbanaltra
　Is bogaim dí an cliabhán.

The tavern is no place for me
　When finished with my labours,
I hurry to the *vanithee,**
　Leave drinking to my neighbours.
They talk of taxes, ale and dearth,
　They're brawling, shouting, mocking,
While I sit by my own clean hearth
　And set the cradle rocking.

DONAL O'SULLIVAN

*From *bhean a' tighe*, woman of the house.

1. I went to the nursing mother's house When the evening mist was falling, And she had nobody for a bedfellow But her pretty little child that was crying.' I asked the nursing mother What made the child to be always wailing; She said that it was usual for him To be whimpering in the night-time.

Chorus. Sleeping while he is being rocked, That is what my fretful baby does, And sleeping while he is being rocked, That is what my fretful baby does!

2. Not so with my own baby, Not a wink does he sleep, And unless daddy kisses its mother The baby will be fretful. Sleeping while he is being rocked, That is what my fretful baby does, And sleeping while he is being rocked, That is what my fretful baby does!

3. I am a domesticated man, I take no pleasure in backbiting, I am a domesticated man, I take no pleasure in contention(?). When the men of the neighbourhood go out To examine their losses(?), I return to the nursing mother And rock the cradle for her.

A BHEAN ÚD THÍOS AR BHRUACH AN tSRUTHÁIN

O WOMAN WASHING BY THE RIVER

A bhean úd thíos ar bhruach an tsrutháin,
  Seó hú leó, seó hú leó,
A' dtuigeann tusa fáth mo ghéaráin?
  Seó hú leó, seó hú leó.
'S gur bliain 's a' lá 'niu fuaduíodh me dhom ghearrán,
  Seó hú leó, seó hú leó,
'S do rugadh isteach me i lios an chnocáin,
  Seó hú leó, seó hú leó.

Seó hín, seó hín, seó hín, seó hín,
  Seó hú leó, seó hú leó,
Seó hín, seó hín, seó hín, seó hín,
  Seó hú leó, seó hú leó.

Seo é annso mo theach mór maiseach,
Is iomdha leann úr is leann sean ann,
Is iomdha mil bhuí 'gus céir bheach ann,
Is iomdha seanduine ar a nasg ann.

Is iomdha buachaill cúl-donn cas ann,
Is iomdha cailín cúl-bhuí deas ann.
Tá dhá bhean déag ag iomchar mac ann,
Tá an oiread eile re n-a n-ais ann.

O woman washing by the river,
  Hushaby, babe not mine,
My woeful wail wilt pity never?
  Hushaby, babe not mine.
A year this day I was snatched for ever,
  Hushaby, babe not mine,
To the green hill fort where thorn-trees shiver,
  Hushaby, babe not mine.

Shoheen, shoheen, shoheen, shoheen,
  Sho-hu-lo, sho-hu-lo,
Shoheen, shoheen, shoheen, shoheen,
  'Tis not thou my baby O!

'Tis there the fairy court is holden,
And there is new ale, there is olden,
And there are combs of honey golden,
And there lie men in bonds enfolden.

How many there, of fairest faces!
Bright-eyed boys, with manly graces!
Gold-haired girls with curling tresses!
There, mothers nurse with sad caresses.

18

Abair lem chéile teacht amáireach,   Ah, bid my husband haste to-morrow,
'S an choinneal chiarach i gcroí a dheárnan,   A waxen taper he shall borrow,
Sgian choise duibhe 'thúirt 'n-a láimh leis,   A black knife bring to cross my sorrow,
'S an capall tosaigh do bhuala 'san mbeárnain.   And stab their first steed coming thoro'.

An luibh a bhuain tá i ndorus an leasa,   Say, pluck the herb where gate-thorns quiver,
Mar shúil re Dia go raghainn leis abhaile;   And wish a wish that God deliver.
Nó mara dtige sé fán tráth sin,   If he come not then, he need come never,
Go mbiad-sa im bainrín ar na mná so.   For they'll make me Fairy Queen for ever!

GEORGE SIGERSON

1. O woman down by the bank of the stream, Sho hoo lo, sho hoo lo, Do you understand the cause of my wailing? Sho hoo lo, sho hoo lo, That this day twelvemonth I was abducted from my palfrey, Sho hoo lo, sho hoo lo, And was carried into the fort of the hillock, Sho hoo lo, sho hoo lo.

Chorus. Shoheen, shoheen, shoheen, shoheen, Sho hoo lo, sho hoo lo, Shoheen, shoheen, shoheen, shoheen, Sho hoo lo, sho hoo lo.

2. This is here my beautiful mansion, There is abundant new ale there and old ale, There is abundant yellow honey and bees-wax there, There is many an old man there held in fetters.

3. Many is the curly brown-haired boy there, Many the handsome fair-haired girl there. There are twelve women bearing sons there, And there are as many more besides them.

4. Tell my husband to come to-morrow, With the wax candle in the centre of his palm, Bringing a black-hafted knife in his hand, And to strike the first horse that comes out of the gap.

5. [Tell him] to pluck the herb that is in the door of the fort, With trust in God that I shall return home with him; Or if he does not come by then, That I shall be queen of these women.

Among the popular superstitions of the Irish there is none more widespread or more firmly held than the belief in an order of magical beings called the *Sluagh Sidhe* (pronounced *Slooa Shee*), who inhabit the prehistoric tumuli or knolls which abound in the country. The Irish word for this type of tumulus is *lios* (pronounced *liss*), generally rendered as "fort". Though the *Sluagh Sidhe* are called "fairies" in English, the translation is not very apposite. The ordinary concept of a fairy is of a diminutive supernatural being, whereas the *Sluagh Sidhe* have the same stature as mortals. Probably the most familiar of these folk is the *bean sidhe* (banshee, woman fairy), whose wail as she combs her hair (usually red) portends death or calamity.

The *Sluagh Sidhe* often sally forth from their dwelling-places, riding on the whirlwind (*sidhe gaoithe*); and one of their activities is the abduction of mortals into the forts: children for those of their number who are childless; handsome young men for husbands; healthy young women to be wives or nursing mothers. In place of the person abducted a changeling may be left—a withered old man or woman or a peevish, sickly child, as the circumstances may require. Various devices might be adopted for securing the return of the abducted; in the case of a child, for example, by putting the changeling to sit on a red-hot griddle. As late as the middle of the last century persons were tried for murder in Tipperary for causing the death of a supposed changeling in this way.

In the present song, a young married woman has been swept from her palfrey and taken into a fort to function as a foster-mother. On the anniversary of that day she is standing at the door of the fort, nursing the child she has been given, when she sees a woman standing on the bank of a stream close by. Under the guise of a lullaby sung to the baby she informs the woman of her abduction, describes the interior of the fort, and asks for a message to be conveyed to her husband with a view to her rescue.

The husband is to carry a wax candle (presumably one of those blessed by the Church at Candlemas) as a protection against the powers of darkness. He is to bring a black-hafted knife, which, according to tradition, is the only weapon capable of prevailing against the

19

Sluagh Sidhe. (A single stab from it was fatal, but a second stab rendered the first one harmless.) The husband is to strike the leading horse as it emerges from the fort, whereupon his wife will be made free; and he is to gather the herb that grows at the entrance, for possession of this is a sure safeguard against recapture. Finally, he is urged to come on the following day, because once a mortal has been in the custody of the *Sluagh Sidhe* for a year and a day all possibility of release is at an end.

DO CHUIRFINN-SE FÉIN MO LEANBH A CHODLA

I'D PUT YOU MYSELF, MY BABY, TO SLUMBER

Grazioso

Do chuir - finn - se féin mo lean - abh a chodl - a,
I'd put you my - self, my ba - by, to slum - ber,

'S ní mar do chuir-feadh mná na mbod-ach, Fá shúis - ín bhuí ná
Not as 'tis done by the clown - ish num - ber, A yel - low blan - ket and

'mbar - al - ín bharr-aigh, Ach i gcliabh - án óir is an ghaoth dhá bhog - a.
coarse sheet bring-ing, But in gold - en cra - dle that's soft-ly swing - ing

CHORUS

Seó hín seó, hú leó leó, Seó hín seó, is tú mo lean-abh!
To and fro, lu la lo, To and fro, my bon - nie ba - by!

Seó hín seó, hú leó leó, Seó hín seó, 's is tú mo lean-abh!
To and fro, lu la lo, To and fro, my own sweet ba - by!

Do chuirfinn-se féin mo leanbh a chodla,
'S ní mar do chuirfeadh mná na mbodach,
Fá shúisín bhuí ná i mbaralín bharraigh,
Ach i gcliabhán óir is an ghaoth dhá bhoga.

> Seó hín seó, hú leó leó,
> Seó hín seó, is tú mo leanbh,
> Seó hín seó, hú leó leó,
> Seó hín seó, 's is tú mo leanbh.

Do chuirfinn-se féin mo leanbh a chodla
Lá breá gréine idir dhá Nodlaig,
I gcliabhán óir ar úrlár shocair,
Faoi bharraí na gcraobh is an ghaoth dhá bhoga.

Codail, a leinbh, 's gura codla slán dhuit,
Is as do chodla go dtugair do shláinte;
Nár bhuailidh treighid ná greim an bháis tú,
Galar na leanbh ná'n bholgach ghránna.

Codail, a leinbh, 's gura codla slán dhuit,
Is as do chodla go dtugair do shláinte;
As do smaointe do chroí nár chráitear,
Is nára bean gan mac do mháthair!

I'd put you myself, my baby, to slumber,
Not as 'tis done by the clownish number—
A yellow blanket and coarse sheet bringing,
But in golden cradle that's softly swinging

> To and fro, lu la lo,
> To and fro, my bonnie baby!
> To and fro, lu la lo,
> To and fro, my own sweet baby!

I'd put you myself, my baby, to slumber
On sunniest day of the pleasant summer,
Your golden cradle on smooth lawn laying,
'Neath murmuring boughs that the birds are swaying

Slumber, my babe! may the sweet sleep woo you,
And from your slumbers may health come to you,
May all disease now flee and fear you,
May sickness and sorrow ne'er come near you!

Slumber, my babe! may the sweet sleep woo you,
And from your slumbers may health come to you,
May bright dreams come, and come no other,
And may I be never a sonless mother!

GEORGE SIGERSON

1. I would myself put my baby to sleep, And not as the wives of rustics do, Under a yellow blanket or a sheet of tow, But in a golden cradle rocked by the wind.

Chorus. Sho-heen sho, hoo lo lo, Sho-heen sho, you are my baby, Sho-heen sho, hoo lo lo, Sho-heen sho, and you are my baby.

2. I would myself put my baby to sleep On a fine sunny day between two Christmases, In a golden cradle on a smooth floor, Beneath the tree-tops and rocked by the wind.

3. Sleep, my baby, sound be your sleep, And from your sleep may you wax in health; May neither colic nor death-stitch strike you, The infants' disease nor the ugly smallpox.

4. Sleep, my baby, sound be your sleep, And from your sleep may you wax in health; By painful dreams may your heart be untroubled, And may your mother not be a sonless woman!

CHILDREN'S SONGS

In some countries—notably in England—there exists a large body of nursery-rhymes and children's singing-games which are found in independent tradition all over the country: such as "Humpty Dumpty", "Ring o' Roses", "Here We Go Looby Loo", and so on; and these form a not unimportant part of folk-song. Such rhymes and games are familiar in all English-speaking countries, Ireland included; but in the Irish-speaking districts the number of nursery-rhymes is comparatively few, and it is doubtful if there are any singing-games with an origin in genuine native tradition. However, one finds in the various localities simple songs of the type that appeal to children and are sung by them, though they have not become universalized so as to cover the whole Gaelic area.

IS TRUA GAN PEATA AN MHAOIR AGAM

I WISH I HAD THE SHEPHERD'S LAMB

Is trua gan peata an mhaoir agam, Is trua gan peat-a'n mhaoir a-gam, Is trua gan peat-a'n mhaoir a-gam, 'S na caoir-e beag-a bán- a.

I wish I had the shep-herd's lamb, I wish I had the shep-herd's lamb, I wish I had the shep-herd's lamb, And Kat-ey com-ing aft- er.

CHORUS

Is Ó! goir-im, goir-im thú, Is grá mo chroí gan cheil-ig thú, Is Ó! goir-im, goir-im thú, 'S tú peat-a beag do mhá-thar!

Iss Ó! gurr-im, gurr-im hoo, Iss grah ma chree gon kell-ig hoo, Iss Ó! gurr-im, gurr-im hoo, Sthoo pa-tha beg dhe wau-her!

Is trua gan peata an mhaoir agam,*
   'S na caoire beaga bána.
	I wish I had the shepherd's lamb,*
	   And Katey coming after.

Is Ó! goirim, goirim thú,
 Is grá mo chroí gan cheilig thú,
 Is Ó! goirim, goirim thú,
   'S tú peata beag do mháthar!
	Iss O! gurrim, gurrim hoo,
	 Iss grah machree gon kellig hoo,
	 Iss O! gurrim, gurrim hoo,
	   Sthoo pa-tha beg dhe wau-her!

Is trua gan maoilín bán agam,
   Is fáilte ó mo ghrá geal.
	I wish I had the yellow cow,
	   And welcome from my darling.

Is trua gan bólacht bainne 'gam,
   Is Caitín ó r. a mháthair.
	I wish I had a herd of kine,
	   And Katey from her father.

TRADITIONAL

*The first line of each verse is to be sung three times.

1. I wish the shepherd's pet were mine, And the little white sheep.
Chorus. And O! I hail you, I hail you, You are my heart's love without deceit, And O! I hail you, I hail you, And you are your mother's little pet!
2. I wish I had a white hornless cow, And a welcome from my bright love.
3. I wish I had a herd of dairy cows, And little Kate from her mother.

25

LEANBH AN CHLAMHRÁIN   A BOLD CHILD

Níl aon leanbh sa' dúthaigh chomh h-aindeis liom, Mo mhá-thair gach
There's no child in the vil - lage so sad as me, My mam-my is

aon lá 'bruín liom! Bíonn m'a-thair am prioc-a 's am sta-tha leis, Níl mo
al - ways com-plain-ing! My dad-dy says no-one's as bad as me, I'm

CHORUS

dhó-thain le n-i-the le mí uaidh! Cum - á ná beir-íon sibh
hun - gry and cold and it's rain - ing! Why don't you boil me

bain-ne dom? Cum - á ná tug-an sibh im dom? Cum-
milk? Why don't you cook some-thing tas - ty?

-á ná téan sibh dhon cha-thair, A' ceann-ach dom luach leath-phing-e chís-dí?
Why don't you go to town, And buy me a ha'-p'orth of pas-try?

Níl aon leanbh sa' dúthaigh chomh h-aindeis liom,
   Mo mháthair gach aon lá a' bruín liom!
Bíonn m'athair am prioca 's am statha leis,
   Níl mo dhóthain le n-ithe le mí uaidh!

Cumá ná beiríon sibh bainne dhom?
   Cumá ná tugan sibh im dom?
Cumá ná téan sibh dhon chathair
   A' ceannach dom luach leath-phinge chísdí?

Mara bhfaghad-sa na císdí ar maidin uaibh
   Fanfad sa' leabaidh go h-oíche,
Ní leogfad do mháthair ná d'athair leis
   Mo cheannín deas cailce do chíora!

Tá mo mháthair gach lá a' gabháil stealla dhom,
   Is m'athair a' gabháil dom istoíche,
Bíonn Síle is Peadar a' maga fúm,
   Is táim marbh ar fad aige Suímon!

Ach gearánfad mo mháthair lem athair,
   Is gearánfa mé m'athair le Síle,
Gearánfa mé Síle le Peadar—
   Is leis a' gcaitín ghearánfa mé Suímon!

Caithidh anáirde go cneasda me,
   Agus deinidh me chuta gan luí orm,
Seinnidh go meidhreach dom poirtín deas
   A chuirfidh me a' raide 's a' rinnce!

There's no child in the village so sad as me,
   My mammy is always complaining!
My daddy says no one's as bad as me,
   I'm hungry and cold—and it's raining!

Why don't you boil me milk?
   Why don't you cook something tasty?
Why don't you go to town
   And buy me a ha'p'orth of pastry?

If I don't get some goodies to-morrow
   I'll stop in my bed till I do,
Then mammy can't comb little goldilocks,
   And neither, dear daddy, can you!

When you're tiny like me nothing pleases,
   I wish I'd a ladder to climb on!
Both Sheela and Peter are teases,
   I won't say what I think about Simon!

But I'll tell about mammy to daddy,
   And I'll tell about daddy to Peter,
I'll tell about Peter to Simon—
   And my pussy will hear about Sheela!

Toss me up high—but don't squeeze me,
   If you like you can tickle me too,
Play me a tune that will please me—
   " *Cosa buí árda* " will do!

Caithidh me anáirde ins na frathacha,
    Agus leigidh dom tuitim chun Síle,
Caith-se, a Shíle, chun Peadair me,
    Agus beir-se me, a Pheadair, a' rinnce!
TADHG Ó CONCHUBHAIR

Toss me as high as the ceiling,
    Sheela will catch me again,
Sheela will throw me to Peter,
    And Peter will dance with me then!
DONAL O'SULLIVAN

And so, all troubles forgotten, they dance around to one of the jolliest slip-jigs you ever could hear —"*Cosa buí árda**" or "Up! little yellow legs", named after the first line of an old ditty to which mothers dandled their babies on their knees. Like this:

1. There is no child in the neighbourhood so miserable as I am, My mother quarrelling with me every day! My father keeps nagging at me and pulling at me too, He hasn't given me enough to eat for a month!

Chorus. Why don't you boil milk for me? Why don't you give me butter? Why don't you go to the town And buy me a halfpennyworth of cakes?

2. If I don't get the cakes from you in the morning I'll stay in bed until evening, I'll not let mother or father Comb my pretty little flaxen head.

3. Every day my mother is pitching on me, And my father pitches on me at night, Sheela and Peter keep making fun of me, And Simon is the death of me entirely!

4. But I'll complain of mother to father, And I'll complain of father to Sheela, I'll complain of Sheela to Peter, And I'll complain to the kitten about Simon!

5. Toss me up high, but go gently, And tickle me without hurting me, Merrily play me a pretty little tune That will set me capering and dancing!

6. Toss me up high to the rafters, And let me fall to Sheela, And, Sheela, you throw me to Peter, And, Peter, you take me dancing!

Tadhg Ó Conchubhair (O'Connor), the author of this charming little piece, was a small farmer at Lispole, some five miles east of Dingle, County Kerry. He died in the winter of 1925, his death being recorded in *An Lóchrann* for January, 1926, where his photograph is printed.

*Pronounced *Cussa bwee awr-dha*.

A MHÁITHRÍN, A' LEIGFEÁ 'UN AN AONAIGH MÉ?

MAMMY, WILL YOU LET ME GO TO THE FAIR?

Allegretto

"A mhái-thrín, a' leig-feá 'un an aon-aigh mé? A mhái-thrín, a'
"Mam-my, will you let me go to the fair? Mam-my, will you

leig-feá 'un an aon-aigh mé? A mhái-thrín, a' leig-feá 'un an
let me go to the fair? Mam-my, will you let me

aon-aigh mé? A mhái-thrín, a' leig-feá 'un an aon-aigh
go to the fair? Mam-my, will you let me go to the

mé?" "A mhúir-nín Ó! ná h-éil-igh é!"
fair?" "My dar-ling dear, I would-n't dare!"

" A mháithrín, a' leigfeá 'un an aonaigh mé? "*
" A mhúirnín Ó! ná h-éiligh é! "

" Beidh aonach i mbárach i gConndae an Chláir.
Cé'n mhaith dom é? Ní bheidh mé ánn."

" Níl tú a deich ná a h-aon déag fós.
Nuair bheas tú trí déag beidh tú mór."

" Mammy, will you let me go to the fair? "*
" My darling dear, I wouldn't dare! "

" There's a fair to-morrow in the County Clare.
No use to me—I sha'n't be there."

" You're not ten yet, nor eleven, my joy.
When you're thirteen you'll be a big boy."

DONAL O'SULLIVAN

*The first line of each verse is to be sung four times.

1. " Little mother, will you let me go to the fair? " " My darling, do not ask it ! "
2. " There will be a fair to-morrow in County Clare. What use is that to me? I shall not be there."
3. " You are not ten or eleven yet. When you are thirteen you will be big."

DÁ bhFAGHAINN MO ROGHA DE THRIÚR ACA

IF I GET MY PICK OF THE THREE OF THEM

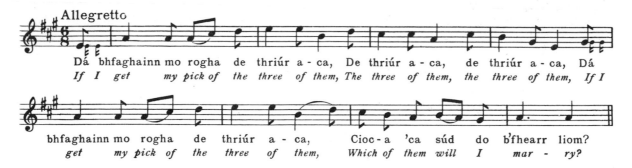

Dá bhfaghainn mo rogha de thriúr aca,
  De thriúr aca, de thriúr aca,
Dá bhfaghainn mo rogha de thriúr aca,
  Cioca 'ca súd do b'fhearr liom?

Ní phósfainn féin an t-iasgaire,
  An t-iasgaire, an t-iasgaire,
Ní phósfainn féin an t-iasgaire,
  Mar bíonn sé fliuch go bhásda.

Ní phósfainn féin an gabha dubh,
  An gabha dubh, an gabha dubh,
Ní phósfainn féin an gabha dubh,
  Mar bíonn sé dubh sa' cheárdchain.

Ní phósfainn féin an táilliúir,
  An táilliúir, an táilliúir,
Ní phósfainn féin an táilliúir,
  Phriocfadh sé mé le n-a shnáthaid!

If I get my pick of the three of them,
  The three of them, the three of them,
If I get my pick of the three of them,
  Which of them will I marry?

I won't marry the sailor,
  The sailor, the sailor,
I won't marry the sailor,
  He always smells so tarry.

I won't marry the blacksmith,
  The blacksmith, the blacksmith,
I won't marry the blacksmith,
  He looks so black and hairy.

I won't marry the tailor,
  The tailor, the tailor,
I won't marry the tailor,
  For he might prick poor Mary!

DONAL O'SULLIVAN

1. If I could get my choice of three of them, Which of them would I prefer?
2. I wouldn't marry the fisherman, For he is always wet to the waist.
3. I wouldn't marry the blacksmith, For he is always black in the forge.
4. I wouldn't marry the tailor, He would prick me with his needle!

SONGS OF OCCUPATION

Songs of Occupation are not found to any considerable extent in Irish collections. But since they do exist it is reasonable to suppose that at one time they were customary all over the country and that, just as in the Scottish Highlands and Western Isles, the men in the fields or the smithy and the women at the spinning-wheel or in the byre would lighten their labours with song. Unfortunately, however, no concerted effort was made to collect both tunes and words at the time when they were in full vigour; and with the increasing mechanization of rural life and the decline of the cottage industries the opportunity has passed. We owe our knowledge of the women's songs very largely to one man, whose name deserves to be remembered: Frank Keane, a Dublin law clerk, who was born at Kilfearagh, near Kilkee, County Clare. He gave the words and music of a number of such pieces to Dr. Petrie, who duly published them; and he wrote down several others in a manuscript from which I printed them some years ago in the Journal of the Irish Folk Song Society.

I give here three women's songs—a Milking Song and two Spinning Songs: and the men are represented by a Plough Song and a Blacksmith's Song. In view of the maritime activity round our coasts—fishing and making a passage to and from the islands—one would naturally expect that boat-songs in Irish would be common enough; but I have never come across even a solitary example.

CRÓNÁN NA BÓ   THE COW'S CHANT

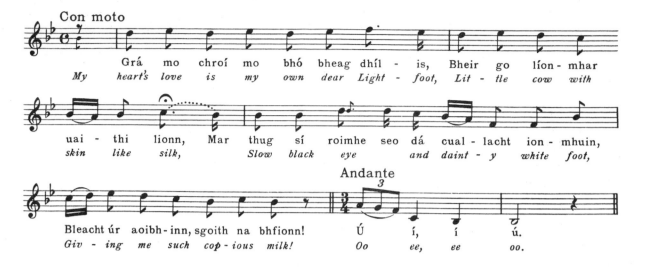

Con moto

Grá mo chroí mo bhó bheag dhíl - is, Bheir go líon-mhar
My heart's love is my own dear Light - foot, Lit - tle cow with

uai - thi lionn, Mar thug sí roimhe seo dá cual - lacht ion-mhuin,
skin like silk, Slow black eye and daint - y white foot,

Andante

Bleacht úr aoibh-inn, sgoith na bhfionn! Ú í, í ú.
Giv - ing me such cop-ious milk! Oo ee, ee oo.

Grá mo chroí mo bhó bheag dhílis,
    Bheir go líonmhar uaithi lionn,
Mar thug sí roimhe seo dá cuallacht ionmhuin,
    Bleacht úr aoibhinn, sgoith na bhfionn!

Do shiúil mé an sliabh duit go moch nuair d'éiríos,
    D'fhéachain a' bhfaghainn tú róm sa' tslí;
Is glasra úra agam i gclúid duit,
    Le gean is dúthracht dom bhó bheag ghroí!

Níl bó i n-Éirinn go mór le chéile
    Is fearr i sgéimh-chruth, snas is snua,
A ceann beag néata is gnaoi le h-éinneach,
    Mo bhó bheag féin is breátha úth!

Is cneasta béasach do sheasuíonn taobh liom,
    'S a liúnacht sgéann le sochar trom;
An t-árthach néata go gcuirtear taobh lé,
    Líontar éasga é le lionn nach gann!

Níl trioblóid éigin dá mbíonn ar éinneach
    Ná sgaipeann sé ón gcroí go deó;
Is teinneas géar-loit, galar is aosdacht,
    Cuireann le chéile iad chun siúil mar cheó!

Mo bhó bheag aonta! Ó táim-se réidh leat,
    Fágaim féin agat mo mhíle slán;
Beannacht Dé leat pé áird a dtéann tú,
    'S nár bhainidh baol duit ná fós mío-cháin!

My heart's love is my own dear Lightfoot,
    Little cow with skin like silk,
Slow black eye and dainty white foot,
    Giving me such copious milk!

At early dawn I roamed the heather
    To seek you in the morning dew,
With bundles tightly bound together
    Of lush green grass—and all for you!

No cow in Ireland's like my treasure
    For shapely head and gentle ways,
Her splendid udder yields full measure—
    Small wonder if I sing her praise!

At milking-time she stands sedately,
    Peaceful as a placid stream,
Set the pail beside her neatly,
    It's quickly filled with milk like cream!

The fear of thirst, the pangs of hunger
    Her full rich milk right swift allays,
Heartens youth, makes old folk younger,
    Grants them peace and length of days!

And now, my pet, the milking's over,
    Goodbye until it comes again!
I'll lead you out to browse in clover,
    God keep you safe in sun and rain!
                                    DONAL O'SULLIVAN

1. My dear little cow is my heart's delight, Yielding such plenteous milk, As she gave erstwhile to her precious calves, Fragrant sweet milk, fair flower of kine!

2. I rose up early and walked the mountain To see if I could find you in my path, With fresh fodder in store for you, And hearty good will to my hardy little cow!

3. There is not a cow in the whole of Ireland Comelier and prettier than her; Her small shapely head pleases the eyes of all, And a splendid udder has my own little cow!

4. Quiet and good she stands beside me, And yields abundant wealth of milk; Let the clean pail be set down beside her, And it is quickly filled with a copious stream!

5. This banishes the fear of want from all And thrusts it from the heart for ever; The pain of wounds, disease and age—It makes them all fade away like mist!

6. My own little cow! Now I have finished, Farewell, and a thousand times farewell! God's blessing be with you wherever you go, And may no hurt or harm ever befall you!

"Cuirim-se chút-sa an sealbhán seó."
"Cuirfead-sa tiúin ar an té tá beó."
"Seán Ó Conaill an buachaillín óg."
"Cuirfead-sa síos go poll na dríbe é,
   Crios don tuí air is léine róin,
Ar mhuin sgeach ghéar ghearr dheilgineach,
   'S dhá chéad dealg go dté 'n-a thóin!
Sop ar siúl é, gliogaram glún é,
   Sála go socair é, 's a bholg go mór,
Leathbhairín sodair é, buailtear fán gcurrach é,
   Seóltar fán mbogach é 's baineadh sé móin! "

"Cuirim-se chút-sa an sealbhán seó."
"Cuirfead-sa tiúin ar an té tá beó."
"Seán Ó Domhnaill an buachaillín óg."
"Cuirfead-sa síos go táirne an fhíona é,
   Crios don tsíoda air is léine Hollónd,
Ar mhuin diallaite óir is airgid,
   Slán go gcasaidh mo chara mear óg!

" Now it's your turn to take part in the game."
" I'll make up a verse and then you do the same."
" Young John O'Connell's the boy I would name."
" Down in the pond I'll give him a ducking,
   Then put him to dry on a blackthorn tree,
With a straw belt on and a shirt of rough smocking
   And a hundred thorns pricking his bottom so free!
He's a knock-kneed, walking wisp of misery,
   With his kibey heels and a belly that sags,
A trotting, half-baked, scrimshank miser he,
   Turn him loose to cut turf, for he's best on the bogs! "

" Now it's your turn to take part in the game."
" I'll make up a verse and then you do the same."
" Young John O'Donnell's the boy I would name."
" Take him down to the inn for wine and feasting,
   Mounted on saddle of silver and gold,
With silken girdle and shirt of Holland,
   And a safe return to my lover so bold!

As sin suas go crois an mhargaidh,   Then back to the market cross bring him over,
 Le maighre cailce 'gus machaire bó,   With a blooming maid and a herd of kine;
Barr mo mhéar le barr a mhéar,   Clasping his hand, I'll walk with my lover,
 Is so-nuachar séin chun mo chara mear óg! " A happy young bride for this sweetheart of mine! "
                      DONAL O'SULLIVAN

1. " I send you the precious treasure." " I will make a song about any living person." " John O'Connell is the young man." " I'll send him down to the muddy hole, A straw belt on him and a hair shirt, Atop of a sharp, low, thorny bush, And may two hundred thorns prick his behind! He's a walking wisp, he staggers at the knees, Easy-heels is he, and his belly is big, He's a trotting half-bake, drive him to the swamp, Lead him to the bog, and let him cut turf! "

2. " I send you the precious treasure." " I will make a song about any living person." " John O'Donnell is the young man." " I'll send him down to the wine tavern, With a girdle of silk and a Holland shirt, On the back of a gold and silver saddle, And a safe return to my limber young lover! Thence up to the market cross, With a beautiful maid and a herd of kine, The tips of my fingers to the tips of his fingers, And a happy bride to my limber young lover! "

In former times it was customary for the young women of a particular locality to meet in each other's houses to discharge the *comhar* (pronounced *core*) or mutual co-operation agreed upon, such as spinning, knitting, sewing and the like. The monotony of the work was relieved by singing, which generally takes the form of a musical dialogue. One girl mentions the name of a young man and another replies, praising him or dispraising him according to her fancy. Other girls contribute their verses in turn, until the work is finished or they grow tired of their pastime or all the eligible young men of the neighbourhood have been passed in review.

The custom, which must be very old, is of course familiar elsewhere than in Ireland. One inevitably recalls the Duke's speech in *Twelfth Night*:

> Now, good Cesario, but that piece of song,
> That old and antique song we heard last night;
> Methought it did relieve my passion much,
> More than light airs and recollected terms
> Of these most brisk and giddy-paced times : . . .
> Mark it, Cesario ; it is old and plain:
> The spinsters and the knitters in the sun,
> And the free maids that weave their thread with bones,
> Do use to chant it; it is silly sooth,
> And dallies with the innocence of love.

The translation of " An Sealbhán Seó " as " The Precious Treasure " is conjectural. Whatever the meaning, the reference is obviously to the tossing of the conversational ball from one girl to another.

35

Allegro moderato

"Cé chuir - fá liúm   ar thaobh na long, Go n-éal-uínn leis   a - nonn?" "Chuir-finn
"Who'll   you give me to   sail   a - way,   And   fare   a - cross   the   sea?"   "I'll

Séam - us leat   ar thaobh na long, Má   éal - óir leis   a - nonn?" "Is
give   you James to   sail   a - way,   And   fare   a - cross   the   sea?"   "A

buach - aill gabhar is caor - ach é,   Is preab - air - e fir   in   aon - bhall é,   Is
shep - herd he   of   fair - est face,   A splen - did fel - low in   ev - 'ry place,   At

rinn - ceóir deas   ar   aon - ach é,   Mar aéir - e cinn   bó   rúin!"
jig   and reel   he   sets   the   pace,   My sweet - heart true   is   he!"

" Cé chuirfá liúm ar thaobh na long,
   Go n-éaluínn leis anonn? "
" Chuirfinn Séamus leat ar thaobh na long,
   Má éalóir leis anonn."
" Is buachaill gabhar is caorach é,
   Is preabaire fir in aon-bhall é,
   Is rinnceóir deas ar aonach é
   Mar aéire cinn bó rúin."

" Cé chuirfá liúm ar thaobh na long,
   Go n-éaluínn leis anonn? "
" Chuirfinn Éamonn leat ar thaobh na long,
   Má éalóir leis anonn."
" Shiúlfainn féin an t-aonach leis,
   Is thiocfainn abhaile im aonar leis,
   Is shínfinn síos im léine leis,
   Ag aéire cinn bó rúin."

" Who'll you give me to sail away
   And fare across the sea? "
" I'll give you James to sail away
   And fare across the sea."
" A shepherd he of fairest face,
   A splendid fellow in every place,
   At jig and reel he sets the pace,
   My sweetheart true is he."

" Who'll you give me to sail away
   And fare across the sea? "
" I'll give you Ned to sail away
   And fare across the sea."
" I'd proudly walk the fair with him,
   I'd shed all fear and care with him,
   My life I'd blithely share with him,
   My sweetheart fond to be."

DONAL O'SULLIVAN

1. " Whom will you put with me aboard ship, So that I may elope with him yonder? " " I shall put James with you aboard ship, If you will elope with him yonder." " He is a goatherd and shepherd, He is a splendid man anywhere, He is a lovely dancer at the fair, The herd of the pet cow."

2. " Whom will you put with me aboard ship, So that I may elope with him yonder? " " I shall put Edmund with you aboard ship, If you will elope with him yonder." " I would walk the fair with him, And I would go home alone with him, And I would lie down in my smock with him, The herd of the pet cow."

This is a dialogue-song of the same type as the previous one. If the girl did not approve of the young man proposed, she would put "Ní" ("Not") in front of what she sang in each verse—"Ní shiúlfainn féin an t-aonach leis" ("I would not walk the fair with him"), and so on.

LOINNEÓG OIREAMH   PLOUGHMEN'S LILT

Brod is buail is tiomáin
Láirín rua na droch-mhná!
Do chos ar an gcéacht, a Thomáis,
   Is féach 'bhfuil ár ndinnéar a' teacht!

Hób a Héin is tiomáin
Láirín rua na deagh-mhná!
Sguir na capaill, a Thomáis,
   Anois tá ár ndinnéar a' teacht!

Goad and strike her now,
   The bad wife's little bay mare!
Your foot upon the plough,
   And see if our dinner is there!

Gently lead her now,
   The good wife's little bay mare!
And let the horses go,
   Now that our dinner is here!

DONAL O'SULLIVAN

   1. Goad and strike and drive The bad woman's little bay mare. Put your foot on the plough, Thomas, And see if our dinner is coming.
   2. Hób and Héin and drive The good woman's little bay mare. Unyoke the horses, Thomas, Now our dinner is coming.

Ploughing takes place at an inclement season of the year, when anything sung might have to compete not only with the trampling of the horses but also perhaps with the noise of the wind and the driving rain. So in our Plough Tunes and Plough Whistles we find a certain wildness, and they are not in general characterized by harmony and rhythm.

Three men were normally engaged in the operation of ploughing, with a team of four horses. No. 1, the *Iománaí* or Driver, led the horses. No. 2, the *Oireamh* or Tailsman, guided the plough and gave directions to the other two. No. 3, the *Tríú Fear* or Third Man, leaned on the head of the plough with a crutch to keep it down, as the tendency of the short chain of the hinder horses was to pull it up.

In this lilt, after the opening chorus of "Hóbó, hóbobo, bó" and so on, the Tailsman sings the first verse. The first half is addressed to the Driver and the second half to the Third Man (Thomas), telling him to take his crutch out of the socket at the head of the plough, to put his foot in its place, and to look up to see if their dinner is coming.

Thomas replies:

        "Tá sé dhá bhuain."   "It is being reaped."

—meaning that the corn for it is being reaped. The Tailsman sings the first verse again at intervals, the Third Man saying after each successive repetition:

        "Tá sé dhá bhuala."   "It is being threshed."

        "Tá sé dhá chátha."   "It is being winnowed."

        "Tá sé dhá chruadha."   "It is being dried."

        "Tá sé dhá mheilt."   "It is being ground."

        "Tá sé dhá chriathra."   "It is being sifted."

        "Tá sé dhá fhuine."   "It is being kneaded."

        "Tá sé dhá iomfhuine."   "It is being thoroughly kneaded."

And finally:

        "Tá sé a' teacht."   "It is coming."

Whereupon the Tailsman sings the second and concluding verse. The terms "Hób" and "Héin" in this verse are words of endearment used in addressing horses.

AN TÁILLIÚIR AERACH   THE FLIGHTY TAILOR

Moderato e ben marcato

Ding dong did-i-lium, buail sin, séid seo, Ding dong did-i-lium, buail sin, séid seo,
Ding dong did-i-lum, blow-er and nail-er, Ding dong did-i-lum, blow-er and nail-er,

Ding dong did-i-lium, buail sin, séid seo, D'im-igh mo bhean leis an táill-iúir aer-ach.
Ding dong did-i-lum, blow-er and nail-er, My wife's gone off with the air-y tail-or.

Ní maith a ním féin tua ná corrán Ní maith a ním féin ramhan ná sleán Ó
I now can't make an axe or spade, I now can't see to ply my trade, Since the

d'im-igh uaim mo stuair-e mná Le gaig-e trua gan bhuar, gan sparán. Ag-us
state-ly girl that once was mine Went off with a fop with-out gold or kine. And

Ding dong didilium, buail sin, séid seo!	*Ding dong didilum, blower and nailer!*
Ding dong didilium, buail sin, séid seo!	*Ding dong didilum, blower and nailer!*
Ding dong didilium, buail sin, séid seo!	*Ding dong didilum, blower and nailer!*
D'imigh mo bhean leis an táilliúir aerach.	*My wife's gone off with the airy tailor.*
Ní maith a ním féin tua ná corrán,	I now can't make an axe or spade,
Ní maith a ním féin ramhan ná sleán,	I now can't see to ply my trade,
Ó d'imigh uaim mo stuaire mná	Since the stately girl that once was mine
Le gaige trua gan bhuar, gan sparán.	Went off with a fop without gold or kine.
A bhean úd thíos an bhrollaigh ghléigil,	Wandering lass of the snow-white breast,
B'fhearra dhuit fille is na builg do shéide	Far better return and take your rest
Ná do ghabha maith féin go bráth a thréigean	With your honest smith for ever and aye
Is triall ris an táilliúir ar fuaid na h-Éireann.	Than roam with the tailor beneath the sky.
Cá bhfuil mo bhuachaill? Buail sin, séid seo!	Where's my 'prentice? Blow and strike!
Cá bhfuil mo neart, is snas mo chéirde?	Where's my skill to shape a pike?
Cá bhfuil mo radharc? Tá'n adharc ar m'éadan	I'm a cuckold now, my trade's a failure
Ó d'éaluigh mo bhean leis an táilliúir aerach.	Since my wife eloped with the airy tailor.
Ding dong didilium, buail sin, séid seo!	*Ding dong didilum, blower and nailer!*
Ding dong didilium, buail sin, séid seo!	*Ding dong didilum, blower and nailer!*
D'imigh mo bhean leis an táilliúir aerach,	*My wife's gone off with the airy tailor,*
Is ní thúrfadh mo chosa me ar sodar fad téide.	*And I stagger around like a drunken sailor.*

DONAL O'SULLIVAN

Chorus. Ding dong didilum, strike that, blow this! My wife has gone off with the flighty tailor.

1. Not well do I make an axe or a sickle, Not well do I make a spade or a slane [turf spade], Since my stately wife has deserted me For a sorry fop without cattle or purse.

2. O white-bosomed woman down yonder, 'Twere better for you to return and blow the bellows Than to leave your own good smith for ever And fare with the tailor throughout Ireland.

3. Where is my boy? Strike that, blow this! Where is my strength, and the nicety of my trade? Where is my sight? The horn is on my brow Since my wife eloped with the flighty tailor.

Last chorus. Ding dong didilum, strike that, blow this! My wife has gone off with the flighty tailor, And my feet would not carry me at a trot for a rope's length.

The music of this blacksmith's song is doubtless far older than the words, and the rhythm of hammer on anvil is well imitated. The crotchets might be taken to represent the sounds made by the sledger with his *órd mór* or sledgehammer and the quavers the blows delivered twice as rapidly by the *lámh-órd* or hand-hammer wielded by the blacksmith himself.

It will be noticed that in the third verse the blacksmith says, "*Tá'n adharc ar m'éadan*" —"The horn is on my brow". The meaning is that he has been made a cuckold by the tailor. In old times cuckolds were fancifully said to wear horns, and the notion is found in many European languages. In England it has been traced as far back as the fifteenth century but is probably older still. The references and allusions in Shakespeare are numerous. Thus Beatrice, indulging in light banter with Leonato, says she will go to the gate of hell, "and there will the devil meet me, like an old cuckold, with horns on his head" (*Much Ado About Nothing*, II, i, 47).

In this as in others of our songs, such as "The Red-haired Man's Wife", the tailor has something of the character of a Lothario, and the reason probably lies in his manner of life. The countryman bought his hand-woven cloth in suit-lengths at the fair and kept it at home against the arrival of the journeyman-tailor, who made the suit on the spot and lived with his customer until it was finished. Hence he was engaged indoors while the man of the house was at work in the fields, the smithy or elsewhere. In the circumstances, the tailor's opportunities for dalliance must have been considerable.

THE SORROWS OF LOVE

The love songs of the Irish are as abundant as those of any other nation; and if the Irish language were more generally known the best of them (and these are very numerous) would be recognized as ranking among the great love songs of the world. It is, indeed, not easy to analyse the characteristics of something which makes so profound and direct an appeal to one's personal emotions; but one finds in these songs a beauty and tenderness beyond the ordinary; a deep and passionate sincerity; a naturalness which disdains all artifice; an exquisite feeling for poetical expression unusual in folk songs; and that candour which is of the essence of intimate human relations between man and woman. Nearly all of them are sad: the outpouring of grief of some sensitive and sorrow-stricken soul who has found, to his cost or hers, the truth of the saying that "the course of true love never did run smooth". Moreover, the melodies to which tradition has wedded them are in perfect concordance with the words.

Of the nine songs which I give here, four are by a man, four are by a girl, and the last is a dialogue between a girl and her dying sweetheart, whom she is soon destined to follow to the grave.

TÁIM SÍNTE AR DO THUAMA

FROM THE COLD SOD THAT'S O'ER YOU

Táim sín-t' ar do thuam-a, 'S do gheóir ann do shíor me; Dá mbeadh
From the cold sod that's o'er you I nev-er shall sev-er; Were my

barr do dhá lámh ag-am Ní sgar-fainn leat choí-che.
hands twined in yours, love, I'd hold them for ev-er. My

'Úil-ín is 'ann-sacht, Is am domh-sa luí leat, Tá
fond-est, my fair-est, We may now sleep to-geth-er, I've the

bol-a fuar na cré orm, Dath na gréin-e's na gaoi-the!
cold earth's damp od-our, And I'm worn from the weath-er!

Táim sínte ar do thuama,
　Is do gheóir ann do shíor me;
Dá mbeadh barr do dhá lámh agam
　Ní sgarfainn leat choíche.
A úilín is a annsacht,
　Is am domh-sa luí leat,
Tá bola fuar na cré orm,
　Dath na gréine 's na gaoithe!

Tá cló ar mo chroi-se
　'Tá líonta le grá dhuit,
Lionndubh ar thaobh thíos de
　Chomh cíordhubh le h-áirne.
Is má bhaineann aon ní dhom
　'S go gclaoifeadh an bás me,
Bead-sa im shí gaoithe
　Romhat thíos ar na bánta!

Nuair is dó le mo mhuinntir
　Go mbím-se ar mo leaba,
Ar do thuama 'sea bhím sínte
　Ó oíche go maidin:
A' cur síos mo chruatan
　'S a' crua-ghol go daingean.
Tré mo chailín ciúin stuama
　Do luadh liom 'n-a leanbh!

From the cold sod that's o'er you
　I never shall sever;
Were my hands twined in yours, love,
　I'd hold them for ever.
My fondest, my fairest,
　We may now sleep together,
I've the cold earth's damp odour,
　And I'm worn from the weather!

This heart, filled with fondness,
　Is wounded and weary,
A dark gulf beneath it
　Yawns jet-black and dreary.
When death comes, a victor,
　In mercy to greet me,
On the wings of the whirlwind
　In the wild wastes you'll meet me!

When the folk of my household
　Suppose I am sleeping,
On your cold grave till morning
　The lone watch I'm keeping:
My grief to the night wind
　For the mild maid to render,
Who was my betrothèd
　Since infancy tender!

EDWARD WALSH

1. I lie on your grave, And you will find me there always; If I had your two hands in mine I would part from you never. My fond one, my dearest, It is time for me to lie with you, The cold smell of the earth is on me, The hue of the sun and of the wind!

2. There is a mark [graven] on my heart That is filled with love for you, While the melancholy beneath it Is as black as a sloe. And if anything happens to me And death were to lay me low, I shall be as a whirlwind Before you, down in the meadows!

3. When my people suppose That I am in my bed, It is on your grave that I am lying From night until morning: Giving vent to my distress And weeping bitterly For my gentle, modest maid That was betrothed to me while yet a child!

AN CLÁR BOG DÉIL   THE SOFT DEAL BOARD

Appassionato

Do ghlac-fainn tú gan ba, gan púint, gan áir-eamh spré, A
I would wed you, dear, with-out gold or gear or count-ed kine, My

chuid 'en tsaol, le toil do mhuinn-tre, dá mb'áil leat mé; 'Sé mo
wealth you'd be, would your friends a-gree, and you be mine; My

ghal-ar dúch gan mé 'gus tú, a dhian-ghrá mo chléibh, I
grief, my gloom! that you do not come, my heart's dear hoard! To

gCais-eal Mumhan 's gan do leab-aidh fúinn ach an clár bog déil!
Cash-el fair, though our couch were there but a soft deal board!

Do ghlacfainn tú gan ba, gan púint,
    gan áireamh spré,
A chuid 'en tsaol, le toil do mhuínntre,
    dá mb'ail leat mé.
'Sé mo ghalar dúch gan mé 'gus tú,
    a dhian-ghrá mo chléibh,
I gCaiseal Mumhan 's gan do leabaidh fúinn
    ach an clár bog déil!

Siúil, a chogair, is tar a chodla
    liom féin don ghleann,
Gheó tú fosca, leabaidh f'hlocais
    is aer cois abhann;
Beidh na srotha a' gabháil thorainn
    faoi ghéagaibh crann,
Beidh an londubh i n-ár bhfochair
    is an chéirseach ann.

Searc mo chléibh do thug mé féin duit,
    agus grá tré rún,
Dá dtigeadh sé do chor sa' tsaol
    go mbéinn féin is tú,
Ceangal cléireach eadrainn araon,
    's an fáinne dlúth—
Is dá bhfeicinn féin mo shearc ag aon fhear
    gheóinn bás le cumha!

Dia Domhnaigh nuair a chínn
    ag an dteampoll í,
Fallaing riabhach is ribín uaithne uirthi
    anún mar ghnaoi,
Agus gúna do sguabfadh
    na gleannta fraoich:
Och! 'sé mo bhuaire mar do luadh liom
    'n-a maighdin í!

I would wed you, dear, without gold or gear
    or counted kine,
My wealth you'd be, would your friends agree,
    and you be mine.
My grief, my gloom! that you do not come,
    my heart's dear hoard!
To Cashel fair, though our couch were there
    but a soft deal board!

Oh, come, my bride, o'er the wild hills' side,
    to the valley low,
A downy bed for my love I'll spread,
    where waters flow;
And we shall stray where streamlets play,
    the groves among,
Where echo tells to the listening dells
    the blackbirds' song.

Love tender, true I gave to you,
    and secret sighs,
In hope to see, upon you and me,
    one hour arise
When the priest's blest voice would confirm my choice,
    and the ring's strict tie:
If wife you be, love, to one but me, love,
    in grief I'll die!

In church at prayer first I saw the fair
    in glorious sheen,
In mantle flowing, with jewels glowing,
    and frontlet green,
And robe of whiteness whose fold of lightness
    might sweep the lea,
Oh, my heart is broken since tongues have spoken
    that maid for me!

Tá úr-phíob ag mo mhúirnín,
     is a bráid mar aol,
A cúilín casta búclaidheach
     a' fás go féar;
'Sé mo chumha nimhe nách san úir síos
     do fágadh mé
Sara stiúiríodh mé i gcúigíbh
     is mo ghrá thar m'éis!

A neck of white has my heart's delight,
     and breast like snow,
And flowing hair whose ringlets fair
     to the green grass flow—
Alas! that I did not early die
     before the day
That saw me here, from my bosom's dear
     far, far away!

EDWARD WALSH

1. I would take you without cows or money or a counted dowry, O my share of the world, with your people's consent, if I were to your mind. It is my black grief that you and I, O passionate love of my breast, Are not in Munster's Cashel with no bed to lie on but a soft deal board!

2. Come, darling, and sleep with me in the valley, You will get shelter, a flock bed and air beside a river. The streams will be flowing past us under the branches of the trees, The blackbird will be close to us, and the song-thrush too.

3. The love of my bosom I gave to you, and secret passion. Would it might happen by life's chances that you and I would be [united], With the clergy's knot betwixt us twain and the binding ring, And if I should see my loved one given to another I should die of grief!

4. On Sunday when I used to see her at church, She wore a striped cloak and a green ribbon for adornment, And a gown that would brush the heathery glens. My sorrow that she was [? not] betrothed to me when a maid!

5. My treasure has a shapely throat and a bosom [white] as lime, Her curling, plaited ringlets reaching down to the grass. My bitter grief that I was not laid in the grave Before I was sent wandering through the provinces [of Ireland], with my love left behind!

PÉARLA AN BHROLLAIGH BHÁIN   THE SNOWY-BREASTED PEARL

Tá cailín deas am chrá
Le bliain agus le lá,
  Is ní fhéadaim a fáil le bréaga;
Níl aiste chlis le rá
Dá gcanaid fir le mná
  Nár chaitheamar gan tábhacht lé-si.
Don Fhrainnc nó don Spáinn
Dá dtéadh mo ghrá,
  Go raghainn-se gach lá dá féachain;
'S maran dúinn atá i ndán
An ainnir chiúin seo d'fháil,
  Och! Mac Muire na ngrás dár saora!

Is a chailín chailce bhláith,
Dá dtugas searc is grá,
  Ná túir-se gach tráth dhom éara;
'S a liacht ainnir mhín im dheáidh
Le buaibh is maoin 'n-a láimh,
  Dá ngabhaimís it áit-se céile.
Póg is míle fáilte
Is barra geal do lámh
  'Sé 'n-iarrfainn-se go bráth mar spré leat;
'S maran domh-sa taoi tú i ndán,
A phéarla an bhrollaigh bháin,
  Nár thí mise slán ón aonach!

There's a colleen fair as May,
For a year and for a day
  I have sought by every way her heart to gain;
There's no art of tongue or eye
Fond youths with maidens try
  But I've tried with ceaseless sigh, yet tried in vain.
If to far-off France or Spain
She'd cross the watery main,
  To see her face again the seas I'd brave;
And if 'tis heaven's decree
That mine she may not be,
  May the Son of Mary me in mercy save!

O thou blooming milk-white dove,
To whom I've given true love,
  Do not ever thus reprove my constancy;
There are maidens would be mine
With wealth in land and kine,
  If my heart would but incline to turn from thee.
But a kiss with welcome bland
And touch of thy fair hand
  Are all that I'd demand, wouldst thou not spurn;
For if not mine, dear girl,
O snowy-breasted pearl,
  May I never from the fair with life return!

GEORGE PETRIE

1. There is a pretty girl tormenting me For a year and for a day, And I cannot win her by cajolery; There is no clever poem that could be mentioned Of the kind that men compose for women That I have not vainly tried with her. To France or to Spain If my love should go, I would fare every day to see her, And if it be not my destiny To win this modest maid, Oh! may Mary's Son of graces save me!

2. And O gentle white girl To whom I have given passionate love, Do not keep ever refusing me; There are many fair maids that seek me, Who possess cattle and treasure, If I would take them to wed in your place. A kiss and a thousand welcomes, And the white tips of your fingers, Are all that I would ever ask as a dowry with you; And if you are not fated to be mine, O pearl of the white bosom, May I not return safe from the fair!

BEAN AN FHIR RUAIDH   THE RED-HAIRED MAN'S WIFE

Tá siad dá rá
  Gur tú sáilín socair i mbróig,
Tá siad dá rá
  Gur tú béilín tana na bpóg.
Tá siad dá rá,
  'Mhíle grá dhil, go dtug tú dham cúl,
Cé go bhfuil fear le fáil,
  'S leis an táilliúirín bean an fhir ruaidh.

Do thugas naoi mí
  I bpríosún ceangailte cruaidh,
Boltaí ar mo chaolaibh
  Is míle glas as súd suas.
Thúrfainn-se sidhe
  Mar thúrfadh eala cois cuain,
Le fonn do bheith sínte
  Síos le bean an fhir ruaidh.

Shaoil mise, a chéad-shearc,
  Go mbeadh aon-tigheas idir mé 's tú,
Shaoil mé 'n-a dhéidh sin
  Go mbréagfá mo leanbh ar do ghlúin.
Mallacht Righ Neimhe
  Ar an té sin bhain dhíom-sa mo chlú,
Sin, agus uile go léir
  Lucht bréige chuir idir mé 's tú.

Tá crann ins an ngáirdín
  Ar a bhfásann duilliúr is bláth buí,
An uair leagaim mo lámh air
  Is láidir nach mbriseann mo chroí.
'Sé mo shólás go bás,
  Is é d'fháil ó fhlaitheas anuas,
Aon phóigín amháin,
  Is é d'fháil ó bhean an fhir ruaidh.

'Tis what they say,
  Thy little heel fits in a shoe,
'Tis what they say,
  Thy little mouth kisses well too.
'Tis what they say,
  Thousand loves, that you left me to rue;
That the tailor went the way
  That the wife of the red-haired man knew.

Nine months did I spend
  In a prison closed tightly and bound;
Bolts on my smalls
  And a thousand locks frowning around.
But o'er the tide
  I would leap with the leap of a swan,
Could I once set my side
  By the bride of the red-haired man.

I thought, O my life,
  That one house between us would be,
And I thought I would find
  You coaxing my child on your knee.
But a curse from on high
  For ever on him let it be,
And the band of the liars
  Who put silence between you and me.

There's a tree in the garden
  With blossoms that tremble and shake,
With my hand on its bark,
  I feel that my heart it must break.
On one wish alone
  My soul through the long months ran,
One little kiss
  From the wife of the red-haired man.

47

Ach go dtig lá an tsaoghail
  'N-a réabfar cnuic agus cuain,
Tiocfaidh smúit ar an ngréin
  'S beidh na néalta chomh dubh leis an ngual.
Beidh an fhairrge tirim,
  Is tiocfaidh na brónta 's na truaighe,
'S beidh an táilliúr a' sgreadach
  An lá sin faoi bhean an fhir ruaidh.

But the day of doom shall come,
  And the hills and the harbours be rent;
Mist shall fall on the sun
  From the thunder-clouds heavily sent;
The sea shall be dry,
  And the earth under mourning and ban;
Then loud shall he cry
  For the wife of the red-haired man.

DOUGLAS HYDE

1. They are saying That you are the dainty little heel in shoe; They are saying That you are the slender little mouth of kisses; They are saying, O thousand loves, that you have turned your back on me, And, though a man is to be had, The red-haired man's wife has gone off with the tailor.

2. I spent nine months In prison, tightly bound, Gyves on my ankles, And a thousand fetters from that up. I would give a leap Like that of a swan beside an inlet, With desire to be lying Down with the red-haired man's wife.

3. I thought, O first love, That there would be one house between you and me; I thought after that That you would be dandling my child on your knee. The curse of the King of Heaven Be on him who took away my character: That, and on all of them, The lying crowd that came between you and me.

4. There is a tree in the garden On which grow foliage and golden blossoms; When I lay my hand on it, My heart almost breaks. It is my solace till death, To get this granted from heaven above, One single little kiss From the red-haired man's wife.

5. When the Day of Judgement shall come, On which hills and harbours will be rent, Mist will cover the sun, And the clouds will be black as coal. The sea will be dry, And trials and tribulations will come, And the tailor will be shrieking On that day because of the red-haired man's wife.

I have found it necessary to make a few slight modifications in Dr. Hyde's charming translation in order to accommodate it to the music.

AN DRAIGHNEÁN DONN

THE BLACKTHORN TREE

Affettuoso

Fuair-eas féir-ín lá aon-aigh ó bhuach-aill deas, Ag-us
I got a fair-ing last fair-day from a hand-some boy, And

céad rud nach é sin ó rogha na bhfear. Sgal-a
plen-ty I don't men-tion from my true love and joy. My bit-ter

cléibh ar an té 'déar-fadh nach tú mo shearc, A bhuach-aill
curse be on the first who de-nies we are one, My hope of

ghléi-gil is breáth' i n-Éir-inn, 's go n-éal-óinn leat!
heav-en! my heart is giv-en to thee a-lone!

Fuaireas féirín lá aonaigh
    ó bhuachaill deas,
Agus céad rud nach é sin
    ó rogha na bhfear.
Sgala cléibh ar an té adéarfadh
    nach tú mo shearc,
A bhuachaill ghléigil is breáth' i n-Éirinn,
    's go n-éalóinn leat!
	I got a fairing last fair-day
	    from a handsome boy,
	And plenty I don't mention
	    from my true love and joy.
	My bitter curse be on the first
	    who denies we are one,
	My hope of heaven! my heart is given
	    to thee alone!

Síleann céad fear gur leó féin mé
    nuair ólaim lionn,
Ní airím iad nuair a smaoinim
    ar a chómhrá liom.
Cúm is míne ná an síoda
    tá'r Shliabh na mBan Fionn,
'S tá mo ghrá mar bhláth na n-áirne
    ar an draighneán donn.
	There's many thinking when I'm drinking
	    that I'm surely theirs,
	But to their pleading I'm unheeding
	    with his whisper in my ears.
	His dear face has all the graces
	    of mountain and of lea,
	And his bosom is like the blossom
	    of the blackthorn tree.

Is glaise súil é ná féar is drúcht air
    's ná duilliúr na gcrann,
Is gile taobh é ná sneachta séite
    ar Shliabh Uí Fhloinn—
Sneachta séite is é dhá shíor-chur
    nó 'tuitim go mall,
'S go bhfuil mo ghrá-sa mar bhláth na n-áirne
    ar an draighneán donn.
	His eye is far brighter
	    than the dew at e'en,
	His side is far whiter
	    than the snow on Slieve Flynn,
	Snow that's pelting or softly melting
	    or falling free,
	And his bosom is like the blossom
	    of the blackthorn tree.

A ógánaigh an chúil dualaigh
    agus é cas ó n-a bharr,
Níl spuaic air ón tsluasaid
    ná mairg ón rámhan.
A Dhia tá thuas, cuireas fuacht
    agus teas ins a' lá,
Gan mé i n-uaigneas na coille dualgaí,
    go nguilfinn mo sháith!
	His curling hair is as fair as
	    the leaves' sun and shade,
	His white hands are unbranded
	    by rough shovel or spade.
	O Creator who makest
	    windy weather and still,
	Lead O lead me where none will heed me,
	    to weep my fill!

Is fear gan chéill bhíos a' dréim leis
    an gcrann a bhíos árd,
Is go bhfuíodh crann beag le n-a thaobh
    dhéanas réidh ar a láimh.
Cé gur árd é an crann caorthainn
    bíonn sé searbh i n-a bharr,
'S go bhfásann sméir is subha craobh ar
    a' gcrann is ísle bláth.

Shaoil mé féin nach 'ceasacht spré orm
    a bheadh grá mo chroí,
'S nach bhfáigfeadh sé 'n-a dhéigh mé
    mar gheall ar mhaoin;
Fó-ríor géar nach bhfuilim féin is
    an té úd a chráidh mo chroí
I ngleanntán sléibhe i bhfad ó éinneach
    is an drúcht 'n-a luí!

Cebé arab oth leis é, molfa mise
    grá mo chroí,
Cebé arab oth leis é, suífe mise
    le n-a thaoibh;
An té lerab oth leis é, míle osna
    tré lár a chroí—
A réalt a' tsoluis, i mbéal gach phobail
    is tú chráidh mo chroí!

A Dhé dhílis! goid é dhéanas mé
    má imíonn tú uaim?
Níl eólas 'un do thighe agam,
    'un do theine nó 'un do chúil.
Tá m'athair faoi leatruim'
    is mo mháthair go dúch,
Fir a' bhaile seo go mór i bhfeirg liom,
    is mo ghrá i bhfad uaim!

A chéad shearc, ná tréig mise
    ar airgead nó ar ór,
'S a chéad shearc, ná tréig mise
    ar mhórán stóir,
A chéad shearc, ná tréig mise
    ar mhacha breá bó,
'S gur tú an chéad fhear dar léig mé leis
    mo rún go h-óg!

Beir leat me— 's níl airgead
    ná ór agam,
Beir leat me— 's níl ba boga
    ar mhóin agam,
Beir leat me— 's níl bábáinín
    óg faoim chrios,
Nó muna mbeirir ní mhairim-se
    bliain ó 'niu!

'Tis but folly to scan holly
    or more lofty trees,
When in the bushes where water rushes
    we find heart's ease.
Though the rowan so high is growing,
    its berry is tart,
While near the ground fruit sweet and sound
    will charm the heart.

Do not neglect me or reject me
    because I'm poor,
Take O take me and ne'er forsake me
    for lack of store!
Would to heaven I were at even
    with him who broke my heart,
With him only, in a valley lonely,
    ne'er, ne'er to part!

Whoso resents it will not prevent it,
    my love's my pride,
Whoso resents it will not prevent it,
    I'll sit by his side.
May who resents it be demented
    and nevermore thrive!
O my dearest, 'tis thou who tearest
    my heart alive!

Son of Mary! without my dearie
    what shall I do?
I cannot meet him, I may not greet him,
    I'm left to rue.
Father, mother, each worse than other,
    sit down and sigh,
Men who'd woo me now look through me,
    and pass me by.

O first love and best love,
    don't look for kine,
O first love and best love,
    though poor I'm thine.
O first love and best love,
    thy love I crave,
O best love, my first love
    to thee I gave!

I'm thine, love, be mine, love,
    and heed not gold,
I'm thine, love, be mine, love,
    nor sheep in fold.
Take me—I've no baby
    as yet unborn,
Take me—shouldst thou forsake me
    I'll die forlorn!

DONAL O'SULLIVAN

1. I got a keepsake on a fair-day from a handsome lad, And a hundred things else from the best of men. A heart-scalding to him who would deny that you are my darling, O radiant youth, Ireland's finest, I would elope with you!

2. A hundred men think I am theirs when I drink ale with them, I heed them not when I ponder on his converse with me. His form is smoother than the silk of Slievenamon, And my love is like the sloe-blossom on the blackthorn tree.

3. His eye is brighter than the dewy grass or the leaves of the trees, His skin is whiter than driven snow on Slieve Flynn, Driven snow thickly falling or gently dropping, And my love is like the sloe-blossom on the blackthorn tree.

4. O my lad with the wavy hair, curling from the very top! His hand is not blistered from the shovel nor swollen by the spade. O God above, Who sendest cold days and hot, Would that I were in the loneliness of the leafy wood, to weep my fill!

5. He is senseless who would strive to climb the lofty tree, While beside it is a little tree, yielding to his hand. Though the rowan tree is high, yet its fruit is bitter, While blackberries and raspberries grow on the trees of lowliest bloom.

6. I thought my love would not find fault with me for lack of dowry, And would not leave me behind him for the sake of riches; Alas! would that I and the boy who broke my heart Were in a lonely valley at the falling of the dew!

7. No matter who grieves at it, I will praise my heart's love, No matter who grieves at it, I will sit by his side. If any grieve at it, may a thousand sighs pierce his heart. O my light-giving star, before all the world you have broken my heart!

8. Dear God! what shall I do if you leave me? I cannot find the way to your house, your fireside, your ingle-nook. My father is afflicted and my mother grieves, All the men here are greatly wroth with me, and my love far away!

9. O first love, do not leave me for silver or gold, O first love, do not leave me for abundance of wealth, O first love, do not leave me for a splendid herd of kine, For you are the first man to whom I have given my young girl's love!

10. Take me with you, and I have neither silver nor gold, Take me with you, and I have no gentle cows on the moorland, Take me with you, and I have no young little baby under my girdle, And if you take me not I shall not live a year from to-day!

'ÓGÁNAIGH ÓIG   YOUNG LAD

'Ogánaigh óig a bhfuil ór in do phéarlaíbh,
Is iomdha cailín óg do phógadh do bhéilín!
Is trua gan mé bheith ag ól leat ar
    bórd i mBinn Éadain,
Agus ór bheith in ár bpócaíbh is sinn pósta le chéile!

'Sé shaoil mise féin (mar bhí mé gan eólas)
Gurbh ionann domh do lámh-sa agus
    fáinne pósta;
Do shaoil mé 'n-a dhéigh sin gur tú an réalt eólais,
Nó mar bhláth na subh-chraobh ar gach taobh do na
    bóithribh!

Is trua Dé gan mise is an giolla dubh
    ar iarraidh
Naoi n-oíche, naoi lá 'gus ceithre ráithe
    na bliana,
I seómra bheith druidthe le fuinneógaibh iarainn,
Glas ar a' dorus is an eochair ar iarraidh!

Is trua géar nach bhfuil mise agus óigfhear na
    súl glas
A' súgra 's ag éisteacht le cléireach ár bpóstaí;
Is cinnte dá mbeadh déannach go mbeinn féin is
    m'óigfhear
A' siúl ar fud coillte le soillse an tráthnóna!

Bhí mé seacht seachtaine ar leabaidh na fuinneóige
Ag éisteacht le n-a aisling is a' féachaint tráth
    chodlódh sé.
Tá dhá bhinn m'fhallainn a' falach gach aon phóige,
'S gurab é grá an radaire tharraing mé 'un trioblóide!

Young lad with the curls and the lips made for kissing,
Would to God you and I from our people were missing,
In a tavern at Howth or abroad in the
    heather,
With gold in our purse, and we wedded together!

I thought, O my love, (I was young and not clever)
That your troth, like a ring, meant you'd part
    from me never:
You seemed after that like the star in my heaven,
Or the raspberry blossom on the roadside
    at even!

Would the dark lad and I were where no one
    could enter,
For nine days and nine nights and from spring
    until winter,
With iron-bound shutters to fasten our chamber,
And the key in a place not a soul could remember!

How I wish that the dark lad and I were both
    kneeling
At the altar in church, with the wedding-bells pealing!
If the clergy were late, be sure I and my dearest
Would roam in the sun through the depths of the
    forest!

Seven weeks by the window a vigil I'm keeping,
As I list to his dreaming and watch him while
    sleeping;
I'm hiding each kiss with my mantle bent double,
And 'tis love for the rascal has brought me to trouble!

'Ógánaigh óig is míne ná an síoda,   Young lad in whose face the shy sunbeam reposes,
Agus d'anál níos cumhrtha ná bola na tíme,   Whose breath is far sweeter than thyme or wild roses,
Do lochta go deó deó ní chuirfinn-se síos duit   I never could blame you, your faults I pass over,
Ach amháin mar fheabhas agus chodlann tú an   Excepting you sleep far too sound for a
         oíche!   lover!

DONAL O'SULLIVAN

1. Young lad with the golden curls, Many a young girl has kissed your small mouth! I would that you and I were drinking at table in Howth, With gold in our pockets, and we wedded together!

2. I thought (for I was innocent) That your plighted troth was the same as a wedding-ring; And then I thought that you were the guiding star, Or the raspberry blossom on each side of the roadway!

3. Would to God that myself and the dark lad were missing Nine nights, nine days and four quarters of the year, In a room closed with iron-barred windows, With the door locked and the key missing!

4. How I wish that I and the young blue-eyed lad Were sweethearting and listening to the priest marrying us! 'Tis certain if he were late that I and my young lad Would be walking through the woods in the afternoon sun!

5. I have spent seven weeks on the window-bed, Listening to his dream and watching while he slept. The two hems of my cloak are hiding every kiss, And 'tis love for the rascal has wrought my undoing!

6. Young lad, you that are softer than silk, Whose breath is sweeter than the scent of thyme, Your faults I would never, never bring against you, Excepting how soundly you sleep at night!

A bhuachaill an chúil_ dual-aigh, Cár_ chod-ail mé 'réir? Ag_
O youth of_ the_ ring-lets, Last_ night as you slept By your

col-ú_ do_ leap-an, 'S níor air- -igh tú mé.
bed-side_ un -heed- ed My_ vig- -il I kept.

Dá mbeadh fios mo cháis ag - at, Ní chodl- ó- fá néal, 'S gur-ab é do
*Did you know of my plight it_ Would trou-ble your rest, That_*

chómh- rá_ binn_ blas- ta D'fhág an os- -na_ so im thaobh.
love_ un -re- qui -ted Is rend- -ing my breast.

A bhuachaill an chúil dualaigh,
   Cár chodail mé 'réir?
Ag colú do leapan,
   'S níor airigh tú mé.
Dá mbeadh fios mo cháis agat,
   Ní chodlófá néal,
'S gurab é do chómhrá binn blasta
   D'fhág an osna so im thaobh.

Nuair luím ar mo leabain
   'Sí m'aisling ochón,
'S ar m'éirghe dham ar maidin
   'Sí mo phaidir mo dheór.
Mo ghruaig bhí 'n-a dualaibh
   Is d'imigh 'n-a ceó,
'Chionn grá 'thúirt don bhuachaill
   Nach bhfuighead-sa go deó!

A bhuachaill an chúil dualaigh,
   Nár fheice mé Dia
Go bhfeicim-se do sgáile
   'Teacht 'dir mé is an ghrian!
Ní thuigeann tú mo mhearú,
   'S ní airíonn tú mo phian,
Is mar bharr ar gach aindeis
   Is leat do chailleas mo chiall!

A bhuachaill an chúil dualaigh,
   An bhfuil ár sonas le fáil,
Nó a' mbeimíd 'n-ár gcomhnuí
   In aon lóisdín amháin?
Sinn araon pósda,
   A stóir 's a dhian-ghrá,
Ár naimhdibh fá bhrón,
   Is ár gcómhgas go sámh!

O youth of the ringlets,
   Last night as you slept
By your bedside unheeded
   My vigil I kept.
Did you know of my plight it
   Would trouble your rest,
That love unrequited
   Is rending my breast.

I sigh through the night as
   I dream of my dear,
When I rise in the morning
   My prayer is a tear.
My spirits are sinking,
   My cheeks pale and wan,
From thinking and thinking
   On him who is gone!

I had rather I'd be, lad,
   For ever unblest
Unless I may see, lad,
   Your head on my breast.
For my passion you care not,
   You heed not my pain—
I could bear it if 'twere not
   It maddens my brain!

O youth of the ringlets,
   Shall we ever find rest
In one household together—
   We twain in one nest?
In wedlock united,
   My darling, my dear,
Our foes all affrighted,
   Our friends without fear!

DONAL O'SULLIVAN

1. O youth of the ringlets, Where slept I last night? At the edge of your bed, And you heeded me not. Had you known of my sad case Not a wink would you sleep, And 'tis your sweet honeyed converse Has left this sigh in my breast.

2. When I lie on my bed My dream is a sob, And on rising in the morning My prayer is a tear. My long flowing ringlets Have vanished like mist, All through loving the lad That will never be mine.

3. O youth of the ringlets, May I never see God Until I see your shadow Coming between me and the sun! You understand not my frenzy And you feel not my pain, And to crown all misfortune It is through you that I have lost my reason!

4. O youth of the ringlets, Shall we ever be blest? Or shall we ever be living In a single dwelling? United in marriage, My darling, my overwhelming love, Our enemies discomfited, And our kinsfolk in tranquillity!

AN CUIMHIN LEAT AN OÍCHE ÚD? YOU REMEMBER THAT NIGHT, LOVE?

An cuimhin leat an oíche úd
  Do bhí tú ag an bhfuinneóg,
Gan hata, gan laimhnne
  Dhod dhíon, gan chasóg?
Do shín mé mo lámh chút,
  'S do rug tú uirthi barróg,
Is d'fhan mé id chomhluadar
  Nó gur labhair an fhuiseóg!

An cuimhin leat an oíche úd
  Do bhí tú agus mise
Ag bun an chrainn chaorthainn
  'S an oíche a' cur chuisne?
Do cheann ar mo chíochaibh,
  Is do phíob gheal dhá seinm,
Is beag do shaoileas an oíche úd
  Go sgaoilfeadh ár gcumann!

A chumainn mo chroí 'stigh,
  Tar oíche ghar éigin,
Nuair luífid mo mhuinntir,
  Chun cainte le chéile.
Beidh mo dhá láimh ad thímcheall,
  Is mé ag innsint mo sgéil dhuit,
'S gurab é do chómhrá suairc mín tais
  Do bhain radharc fhlaithis Dé dhíom!

Tá an teine gan choigilt
  Is an solus gan mhúcha,
Tá an eochair faoi an ndorus,
  Is tarraing go ciúin í.
Tá mo mháthair 'n-a codla
  Agus mise im dhúiseacht,
Tá m'fhoirtiún im dhorn,
  Is mé ullamh chun siúil leat!

You remember that night, love,
  You stood at my casement,
With no glimmer of light, love,
  From attic to basement?
Your voice sweet and gentle,
  Your strong young arms round me,
And I stayed with you then till
  The morning star found me!

You remember that night, love,
  The leaves were our pillow,
When the snow lay so white, love,
  Beneath the green willow?
Your head on my breast, then,
  You gave me love's token,
'Twas little I guessed then
  Our bond would be broken!

Come, sweetheart, come soon when
  My people are sleeping,
By the light of the moon then
  Our tryst we'll be keeping.
Between our embraces
  My pledge will be given,
Though the light in your face has
  Deprived me of heaven!

The lamp is still burning,
  The embers still glowing,
With the key softly turning
  There's none will be knowing.
My mother sleeps calm and
  I wait here still waking,
My dower's in my palm and
  I'm yours for the taking!

DONAL O'SULLIVAN

56

1. Do you remember that night When you were at the window, With neither hat nor gloves Nor coat to shelter you? I reached out my hand to you And you ardently grasped it, And I remained in your company Until the lark began to sing!

2. Do you remember that night When you and I were At the foot of the rowan tree In the freezing night? Your head on my breasts, And your pipe sweetly playing; I little thought that night That our bonds of love would loosen!

3. O beloved of my inmost heart, Come some night, and soon, When my people are abed, That we may talk together. My two arms shall be round you While I tell you my story, For your pleasant, gentle, soft converse Has taken from me the sight of God's heaven!

4. The fire is unraked, And the light is unextinguished, The key is under the door, And pull it out gently. My mother is asleep, And I am fully awake, My fortune is in my hand, And I am ready to go with you!

(*Cailín*)
" Is mo ghrá go léir tu, agus Dé do bheatha chúm!
  Mo ghrá do shúile, agus t'éadan leathan geal,
  Mo ghrá do chroí, nár smaoing ar mh'atharrach,
  Mo ghrá mh'fhear óg, 's is é mo bhrón bheith
      sgartha leat! "

(*Fear*)
" Níl id ghrá-sa ach mar a bheadh mám 'en
     tsneachta 'muigh,
  Nú cúr lae Márta, 'chaithfeadh caise dhe,
  Nú puis den ghaoith thig do dhruím na fairrge,
  Nú tuile shléi bheadh t'réis lae fearthanna! "

(*Cailín*)
" 'S cá bhfeacaís mo ghrá-sa ná mo pháirt let
    atharrach?
  Ná dul ag ól leó ar bhórd go ceanasach?
  Mar nár smaoingeas im chroí ná im aigne
  Luí 'n-a gclúid, agus gan tú bheith ceangailthe."

(*Fear*)
" 'S go deimhin, a mhianaigh, níor smaoingeas
    masla dhuit,
  Ná tú breith liúm gan cead ód bhantharlain,
  'Dtaobh gan amhras gur bh'fhearr liom agam tu
  Ná'n dá asbal déag, is ná maor an
    anama."

(*Cailín*)
" Glaéidh ar Dhia go dian chun t'anama,
  'S ar a' Maighdean Naomhtha, 'sí céile is
    fearra dhuit,
  'Sí thúrfaidh saor tú lá dhaortha an anama;
  Séan mo ghrá-sa 'gus mo pháirt 'n fhaid a
    mhairfe tú!

(*She*)
" You are my heart's love, and how I welcome you!
  I love your eyes, and your bright open countenance,
  I love your heart, that ne'er thought of another,
  My beloved young man, 'tis my grief we are
    parted! "

(*He*)
" There's nought in your love but of snow just a
    handful,
  Or the spray cast in March at the foot of a waterfall,
  Or a catspaw of wind that the smooth sea is ruffling,
  Or a mountainy stream that the rain makes a torrent! "

(*She*)
" And when did you see me show love for
    another?
  Or sit with them drinking at table so merrily?
  For never in life did I wish for their company,
  E'en though you and I had not yet been betrothéd! "

(*He*)
" Indeed then, my darling, I never thought ill of you,
  Nor would claim you for mine without leave
    from your mother,
  Though truly I swear I would rather possess you
  Than God's chosen twelve or my soul's Angel
    Guardian."

(*She*)
" Pray to the Lord that your soul may gain heaven,
  And the Blessed Virgin, the spouse that is best
    for you;
  'Tis she is your shield on the dread Day of Judgement;
  As long as you live, you must shun my
    affection! "

(*Fear*)
" Ní shéanfad do ghrá-sa ná do pháirt 'n fhaid a
     mhairfe mé,
  Ná go ceann seacht mbliain t'réis dul 'on
     talamh dom;
  Mar níor shín do chéile riamh fós ar leabaidh leat,
  'S go deimhin, nuair a shínfidh, sínfead-sa
     eadaraibh! "

(*Cailín*)
" 'S nách gránda an fuath é, t'réis muarán ceanais
     duit,
  Cuir mh'fhir phósda go deó deó i n-earraid liom,
  A' troid 's a' coimheascar, a' bruíon 's ag acharann,
  'S gan tusa beó 'gam chun mo sgéal duit 'aithris! "

(*He*)
" As long as I live, I'll ne'er shun your affection,
  Nor for seven long years when the grave has
     received me.
  For your newly-wed husband has never yet lain
     with you,
  And I swear, when he does, that you'll find me
     between you! "

(*She*)
" How wicked and hateful, when I was so fond
     of you,
  To come between me and my husband for ever,
  Making him jealous and angry and quarrelsome,
  When you're no longer alive for me to confide in! "

DONAL O'SULLIVAN

1. " I love you wholly, and welcome you are to me! I love your eyes, and your open bright forehead, I love your heart, that never thought of anyone but me. My beloved young man, 'tis my grief we are parted! "

2. " Your love is no more than a handful of snow, Or the foam cast by a stream on a March day, Or a puff of wind on the surface of the sea, Or a mountain torrent after a day of rain! "

3. " And when have you seen me show love or fondness for any but you? Or sit drinking with them affectionately at table? For my heart never wished and my mind never fancied Their company, though I was not bound to you."

4. " Truly, my darling, I did not mean to insult you, Or to carry you off without your mother's leave, Although in truth I would rather possess you Than the twelve apostles or the guardian of the soul! "

5. " Pray to God earnestly for your soul, And to the Blessed Virgin, she is the best spouse for you; She it is who will save you on the day when souls are judged, Renounce my love and affection as long as you live! "

6. " I never will renounce your love and affection as long as I live, Nor for seven years after I am laid in the earth; For your husband has never yet lain in bed with you, And truly, when he does, I will lie between you! "

7. " What hateful wickedness, after all my fondness for you, To set my husband at enmity with me for ever, Quarrelling and scolding me, being angry and cross with me, When I shall not have you alive to tell my troubles to! "

My friend Mr. A. Martin Freeman, who noted this touching song in County Cork, published with it his translation of an explanatory note given in connection with another version, obtained in Kerry. I reproduce it here with his permission.

According to this note, the girl's parents married her to a rich man, her lover being poor. The rich fiancé knew nothing of the girl's love for another. When the poor man heard that his sweetheart was to be married, "the weakness of death came upon him, and he lay down to wait for the parting of his soul and body. Well, the engaged couple were married one morning, and that same morning the young woman was told that her best-beloved was on his death-bed. So she said to her husband, 'Oh,' said she, 'a great friend of mine is very sick to-day, and I should like to go and see him.' 'Very well,' said he, 'go along,' thinking it was a good sign in his wife to be going to see a sick person on the very day of her marriage. She went to the house where the sick man lay, and went up to the bed and threw herself on her knees, and looked lovingly at him, speaking as follows:

[*Here follows the dialogue in verse.*]

For he had died while she was saying this last verse. Then she lay down by his side and died too. The neighbours said they ought to be buried in one grave; but when her husband heard the whole story he would not agree to this. Indeed, he buried his wife as far away from the body of her lover as was possible in that churchyard. But soon two trees sprung up, one out of his grave and one out of hers.' They grew upwards and bent towards each other, till there came five fingers, as it were, on the top of each tree, and these fingers interlocked."

Hence the title of "The True Lovers' Knot". The notion is a familiar one in the folk lore of many countries and is identified in Scotland and England with the well-known ballad of "Lord Thomas and Fair Eleanor".

> The tane was laid in Mary's kirk,
>   An' the tither in Mary's quere,
> An' fae the tane there sprang a birk,
>   Fae the ither sprang a brier.
> An' aye they grew an' waxèd strong,
>   Till their heids plait ither near,
> An' by that same ye micht hae kent
>   They twa were lovers dear.

I have found it impossible to render this poem into rhymed verses without spoiling the essential simplicity of the original. Instead, I give a translation in rhythmical prose which is in the same metre.

CUISLE MO CHROÍ PULSE OF MY HEART

Ar maidin indé roimh ghréin go moch,
Do dhearcas an bhé ba néimhe cruth:
  Bhí sneachta 'gus caor
  A' caismirt 'n-a sgéimh,
'S a seanga-chorp séimh mar ghéis ar sruth—
    'S a chuisle mo chroí, créad í'n ghruaim sin ort?

Ba bhinne guth caomh a béil le sult
Ná Orpheus do léig go faon na tuirc:
  Bhí a reamhar-rosg réidh
  Mar chriostal na mbraon
Ar sheamair ghlais f héir roimh ghréin go moch—
    'S a chuisle mo chroí, créad í'n ghruaim sin ort?

Before the sun rose at yester-dawn
I met a fair maid adown the lawn:
  The berry and snow
  To her cheek gave its glow,
And her bosom was fair as the sailing swan—
    Then, pulse of my heart, what gloom is thine?

Her beautiful voice more hearts hath won
Than Orpheus' lyre of old had done:
  Her ripe eyes of blue
  Were crystals of dew
On the grass of the lawn before the sun—
    And, pulse of my heart, what gloom is thine?

EDWARD WALSH

1. Yesterday morning, shortly before sunrise, I beheld a maiden of most glorious form: The snow and the rowan berry Were struggling for mastery in her face, And her fair slender body was like swan on stream —And, O pulse of my heart, what is this gloom that is on thee?

2. The gentle tones of her voice were more delightfully melodious Than [the lyre of] Orpheus who subdued the wild boars: Her soft clear eyes Were like crystal dew-drops On the green shamrock of the meadow, shortly before sunrise—And, O pulse of my heart, what is this gloom that is on thee?

ÚR-CHNOC CHÉIN MHIC CÁINTE

KILLIN'S HILL OF FAERY

Moderato

A phlúr na maigh-dean is úir-e gné, Thug clú is sgéimh ón
O flower of maid-ens of fair-est face, Most love-ly of Eve's

Ádhamh-chloinn, A chúl na bpéar-laí, a rún na h-éig-se,
daugh-ters, Of match-less beau-ty, charm and grace, Bright

Dhúb-luíos féil' is fáil-te: A ghnúis mar ghréin i
jew-el of Mourne's wa-ters: Whose laugh-ter like the

dtús gach lae ghil, Mhúch-as léan le gáir-e, 'Sé mo
ris-en sun Aye cheers the sad and wea-ry, 'Twere

chumha gan mé 's tú, a shiúr, linn féin San dún sin Chéin Mhic Cáin-te!
bliss with you, dear heart, a-lone On Kill-in's hill of faer-y!

A phlúr na maighdean is úire gné,
    Thug clú is sgéimh ón Adhamh-chloinn,
A chúl na bpéarlaí, a rún na h-éigse,
    Dhúbluíos féil' is fáilte:
A ghnúis mar ghréin i dtús gach lae ghil,
    Mhúchas léan le gáire,
'Sé mo chumha gan mé 's tú, a shiúr, linn féin
    San dún sin Chéin Mhic Cáinte!

Táim brúite i bpéin, gan suan gan néal,
    Dod chumha, a ghéag is áille,
'S gur tú mo raoghan i gcúigíbh Éireann,
    Cúis nach séanaim ás de.
Dá siúlfá, a réalt gan smúid, liom féin,
    Ba súgach saor mo shláinte;
Gheóir plúr is méad is cnuasach craobh
    San dún sin Chéin Mhic Cáinte!

Cluinfir uaill na ngadhar ar luadh i ndéidh
    Bhriain luaimnigh bhearnaigh i bhfásaibh,
Is fuaim guth béil bhinn cuach is smaolach
    Suairc ar ghéaga i n-áltaibh:
I bhfuar-linn tséimh chífir slua-bhuíon éisc
    A' ruaga a chéile ar shnámh ann,
'S a' cuan gur léar dhuit uaid i gcéin
    Ón úr-chnoc Chéin Mhic Cáinte!

A shuairc-bhean tséimh na gcuach-fholt péarlach,
    Gluais liom féin ar ball beag,
Tráth is buailte cléir is tuata i néaltaibh
    Suain faoi éidí bána.
Ó thuaidh go mbéam 'bhfad uatha araon
    Teacht nua-chruth gréine amárach,
Gan ghuais le chéile i n-uaigneas aerach
    San uaimh sin Chéin Mhic Cáinte!

PEADAR Ó DOIRNÍN

O flower of maidens of fairest face,
    Most lovely of Eve's daughters,
Of matchless beauty, charm and grace,
    Bright jewel of Mourne's waters:
Whose laughter like the risen sun
    Aye cheers the sad and weary,
'Twere bliss with you, dear heart, alone
    On Killin's hill of faery!

How sad my fate, disconsolate,
    Consumed by love's fond yearning
For her I long for soon and late,
    All other maidens spurning.
O come with me, my guiding star,
    Forsaking farm and dairy,
Where mead and spreading branches are,
    On Killin's hill of faery!

'Tis there you'll hear the noisy hounds
    The nimble hare pursuing,
The thrush's sweet harmonious sounds,
    The gentle stock-dove cooing.
You'll see the trout in limpid stream,
    So sportive, yet so wary,
And view Dundalk as in a dream
    From Killin's hill of faery!

Fond love, to-night a tryst let's keep,
    And stray awhile together;
With priests and layfolk bound in sleep,
    We'll lie among the heather.
To-morrow's sun will find us still
    Upon that spot so airy,
Remote from every harm and ill
    On Killin's hill of faery!

DONAL O'SULLIVAN

64

1. O flower of maidens of freshest face, Sole honour and beauty of Adam's line, O head of curls, O beloved of the bards, Most generous, most hospitable : O face like the sun of a shining morning, Quenching grief with laughter, How I wish that you and I were alone together, dear heart, Within that fort of Cian mac Cáinte !

2. I am bowed with grief, bereft of sleep, Through longing for you, most lovely lass, For 'tis you are my choice in the provinces of Ireland, I proclaim it freely. If you will come with me, O star without mist, Joyous and free will be my health; You will have flour and mead and clustering branches Within that fort of Cian mac Cáinte !

3. You will hear hounds give tongue as they speed in the wake Of nimble, cleft-lipped Brian [the hare] in the thickets, And the sound of the melodious voices of cuckoos and merry thrushes In the branches of the glens : In the placid cold pool you will see numbers of fish, Chasing each other as they swim there, And the distant bay will be clear to view From the verdant hill of Cian mac Cáinte !

4. Merry fair maid of the ringletted curls, Come with me for a little while, When priests and layfolk are bound in slumber Under white coverlets. We shall be northward away from them all When the sun rises newly to-morrow, Free from danger together in the breezy solitude Of that cave of Cian mac Cáinte !

This melodious and well-turned poem was written by Peadar Ó Doirnín (1684–1768), one of the most prolific and perhaps the most accomplished of the South Ulster poets of the eighteenth century. (The English form of his name would be Peter O'Durnin.) He was born near Dundalk, County Louth, and died at Forkhill, County Armagh, and he spent most of his life as a hedge-schoolmaster in these two counties. The Penal Laws were then in full vigour in that part of Ireland, and Catholics were rigorously excluded from the profession of teaching. Hence Ó Doirnín's existence tended to be nomadic and hazardous.

Cnoc Chéin Mhic Cáinte, to which the poet wished to bring his sweetheart, is a pleasant rounded hill about two miles north-west of the town of Dundalk, its modern name being Killin. Though it is not very high, it commands a charming view of Dundalk Bay (referred to in the third verse), as well as of the hills round Carlingford and the Mourne Mountains.

Cian Son of Cáinte, who gives his name to the hill, on the summit of which (according to tradition) he lies buried, is a celebrated character in Irish mythology. It is his slaying by the three sons of Tuireann that makes the starting-point of the famous Irish hero-tale entitled "*Oidhe Chloinne Tuireann*" or "Fate of the Children of Tuireann", which is reckoned as one of the "Three Sorrows of Story-telling". There was formerly a prehistoric monument on the reputed site of the grave of Cian, and this is doubtless the "fort" or "cave" mentioned by our poet. But it was partially demolished by vandals a little more than a century ago.

Andante

Ó! maid-in aoibh-inn uaibh-ir-each Ar bhruach na coill-e's
As I roved out one morn-ing Down by a clear

glais-e bláth, Bhí mo ghadhair-ín liom a' gluais-eacht Go
riv-er side, With dogs and gun com-mand-ing In

h-uas-al is mo ghunn' im láimh. Cas-adh or-am
de-cent and be-com-ing pride, I spied a love-ly

stu-a-bhean Ba ru-aidhe ghil-e dheis-e bhreá, Ag-us
crea-ture Whose fair locks I chanced to view, With a

bir-tín léi-thi buail-te Dhen luach-air ba dheis-e bláth.
bunch of rush-es mak-ing, As pleas-ing as ev-er grew.

Ó! maidin aoibhinn uaibhreach
  Ar bhruach na coille is glaise bláth,
Bhí mo ghadhairín liom a' gluaiseacht
  Go h-uasal is mo ghunna im láimh.
Casadh orm stua-bhean
  Ba ruaidhe ghile dheise bhreá,
Agus birtín léithi buailte
  Dhen luachair ba dheise bláth.

Is d'fhéachas ar na cuantaibh,
  'S do bhí an t-uaigneas againn um neóin,
Do dhruideas leis an stuaire
  Is d'fhuaduíos uaithi cúpla póg.
'Sé dúirt sí liom go h-uaibhreach,
  " Fan uaim is ná cuir orm stró,
'S ná sgaip mo bheinnsín luachra
  Is a bhfuaireas dá thrioblóid."

" A chailín bhig na luachra,
  A' leigfeá-sa do bheart ar lár?
Nó a' dtiocfá liom i n-uaigneas
  Faoi bhruach na coille is glaise bláth?
Sagairt ní bhfuíodh sgéal air,
  Nó éinneach dá bhfuil le fáil,
Go dtiocfaidh cainnt don chéirseach
  Nó béarla don londubh bhreá."

" A chailín bhig na luachra,
  Glac suaineas is fan go réidh;
Ní cáll duit a bheith uaibhreach
  I n-uaigneas is tú leat féin.
Má sgaip mé do chuid luachra,
  Is dual go bhfuil cuid tar h'éis;
Bainfead beinnse muar dhuit,
  Is ualach mar thuille léi."

As I roved out one morning
  Down by a clear river side,
With dogs and gun commanding
  In decent and becoming pride,
I spied a lovely creature
  Whose fair locks I chanced to view,
With a bunch of rushes making,
  As pleasing as ever grew.

I looked about most careful,
  The place being free and clear,
I used some kind endeavours
  With this fair maid I loved so dear.
She said, " Kind sir, be easy,
  I am a maid, you needs must know,
These rushes cost some labour,
  So spare them and let me go."

I said, " My charming creature,
  Be pleasing to me and kind,
This moment is the season
  That engages my tender mind.
These rushes cost some labour,
  'Tis plain that the like do grow;
Then grant me your kind favour,
  Embrace me and ease my woe."

I gently did embrace her,
  In my arms I did her entwine;
" If your parents they are pleased now,
  In wedlock's bands we will join.
My heart you've captivated
  On this place where the rushes grow,
And for ever I'll embrace you,
  And your bonny bincheen luachara O!"

TRADITIONAL

66

1. On a delightful gay morning By the fringe of the wood of greenest blossom, My little dog was walking with me Proudly, and my gun was in my hand, When I met a graceful girl, Red-haired, radiant, most beautiful and fair, Clasping a bundle Of rushes of finest blossom.

2. I gazed on the landscape, And we were in solitude at noon, I approached the maid And stole from her a couple of kisses. She said to me haughtily, " Leave me alone and do not dally with me, And do not scatter my bundle of rushes That I gathered with such trouble."

3. " O little girl of the rushes, Will you leave your bundle down? And will you come with me in solitude To the fringe of the wood of greenest blossom? The priests will not hear of it, Nor anyone at all, Till talk comes to the song-thrush And speech to the handsome blackbird."

4. " O little girl of the rushes, Be tranquil and stay quiet; There is no need for you to be haughty In solitude, all alone. If I have scattered your rushes, It is natural that there are more of them; I shall gather a great bundle for you, And a load of them for good measure(?)."

This is one of the best-known of Irish Gaelic songs, and numerous versions exist of both words and air. The beautiful tune here given may well be thought to be worthy of a better theme; at the same time, the excellent assonance of the original makes the poem a melodious one.

The girl was presumably gathering rushes for thatch or for carpet-making, but her bundle has the same symbolical meaning as thyme in English folk song, such as the familiar verse in "The Seeds of Love":

> I once had a sprig of thyme,
>   It prospered night and day,
> By chance there came a false young man
>   And he stole my thyme away.

A popular Irish song was sometimes given an English dress and issued as a broadsheet; and in this case I give the broadsheet version in place of a strict metrical translation of the original. The humble and unknown translators of such pieces knew Irish well, but their knowledge of English prosody was far to seek; and so, probably quite unconsciously, they imitated the assonance of their originals. To realise this to the full, one must bear in mind that the pronunciation is that of the Irish countryside—"daycent" for "decent", "crayture" for "creature", "plaising" for "pleasing", "aisy" for "easy", and so on. The internal assonance then becomes obvious. To take the third verse as an example:

> I said, 'My charming crayture,
>   Be plaising to me and kind,
> This moment is the saison
>   That engages my tender mind.
> These rushes cost some labour,
>   'Tis plain that the like do grow ;
> Then grant me your kind favour,
>   Embrace me and aise my woe'.

INGHEAN AN PHAILITÍNIGH

THE PALATINE'S DAUGHTER

Scherzando

Ó!__ lá breá aoibh-inn mar-a-gaidh's mé a' gabhail thrí Bhail' Ó
As__ I roved out one even-ing through the groves of Ball-y-

Síod - a Ri ti i-dle oo-dle, Day ri fol de dee-dle,
-seed - y Ri ti i-dle oo-dle, Day ri fol de dee-dle,

Ti ri i-dle oo-dle, Tol di o, Cé cas-faí ins a'
Ti ri i-dle oo-dle, Tol di o, Whom should I meet on a

tslí orm ach in-ghean a' Phail-it-ín-igh?
cool re-treat but an I-rish Pal-a-tine's daugh-ter?

Ri ti i-dle oo-dle, Day ri fol de dee-dle, Ti ri i-dle oo-dle,
Ri ti i-dle oo-dle, Day ri fol de dee-dle, Ti ri i-dle oo-dle,

Tol di o. Ó! d'fhios-ar-uigh sí fios m'ain-im-e, "nó goid-
Tol di o. She asked my name and sta-tion, O! or__

-é an bail' ó go mbíonn tú? A' dtioc-fá féin a-bhail-e liom__
where was my dwell-ing ar-bour, Or would I come a-long with her to

seal i dtigh mo mhuinn-tre?" 'Sé_ dubhart, "Is buach-aill grean-ta mé do
see her own dear fa-ther. I__ said I was a rak-ish lad, in

chomhn-uíonn i gCoir-ín-ibh," Ri ti i-dle oo-dle,
Cur-rans I was in ser-vice, Ri ti i-dle oo-dle,

Day ri fol de dee-dle, Ti ri i-dle oo-dle, Tol di o.
Day ri fol de dee-dle, Ti ri i-dle oo-dle, Tol di o.

Ó! lá breá aoibhinn maragaidh
   's mé a' gabháil thrí Bhail' Ó Síoda,
Cé casfaí ins a' tslí orm ach
   inghean a' Phailitínigh?
Ó! d'fhiosaruigh sí fios m'ainime,
   " nó goidé an baile ó go mbíonn tú?
A' dtiocfá féin abhaile liom
   seal i dtigh mo mhuinntre? "
'Sé dubhart, " Is buachaill greanta mé
   do chomhnuíonn i gCoirínibh."

" Má thréigeann tú an t-aifreann
   do gheó tú mé le pósa,
Mar a dhein mo cháirde féinig is
   a maireann eile beó aca.
Ghéo tú ór is airgead
   is talamh gan aon chíos liom,
Agus litir ó *Mhister Oliver*
   go bhfuil m'athair caithte, críonna,
Is cailín deas chun taistil leat,
   más meón leat Pailitíneach."

Do dhruideas-sa 'n-a h-aice siúd
   is do thugas dí cúpla póigín:
" Is má théim-se féin abhaile leat
   an bhfagha mé tú le pósa?"
'Sé dubhairt sí, " Ná bíodh eagal ort,
   tair liom is míle fáilte,
Is gheó tú le toil m'athar mé,
   's gan dearmad mo mháithrín,
Ghéo tú stoc ar thalamh liom
   is mairfimíd go sásta."

Is anois tá mo dhuainín críochnuithe
   's gan peann ná dubh im dhearnain,
Do thug sí an t-óigfhear barrfhionn lé
   abhaile go dtí n-a máthair.
Do chríochnuíodar an maraga
   is bhí sé annsan 'n-a mháistir,
Fuair sé tigh is talamh lé
   'gus iothala chluthmhar shásta,
Is annsan do dhein sé Caitliceach
   den ainnir mhilis mhánla.

As I roved out one evening through
   the groves of Ballyseedy,
Whom should I meet on a cool retreat
   but an Irish Palatine's daughter?
She asked my name and station O!
   or where was my dwelling arbour?
Or would I come along with her
   to see her own dear father?
I said I was a rakish lad,
   In Currans I was in sarvice.

" If you forsake the Mass and sacraments
   you'll get me and my portion,
As I have done in person and
   my forefathers before me.
You'll get gold and silver O!
   and land without tax or charges,
And a letter from Mister Oliver
   my father's unfit for sarvice,
And a pretty lass to wed with you,
   if you choose a Palatine's daughter."

I courteously saluted her
   And twice I kissed my darling:
" And if I go home along with you
   shall I get you as my partner?"
She said, " A thousand welcomes O!
   and be not the least alarmèd,
You'll have my mother's blessing and
   best wishes of my father,
You'll get stock and property,
   and we'll be happy ever after."

And now my song is ended and
   my pen is out of order,
She brought this handsome young man
   in presence of her father.
They agreed and soon got married O!
   and then he became master,
He got his landed property,
   his haggard and his barn,
And then he made a Catholic
   Of the Irish Palatine's daughter.

TRADITIONAL

1. On a fine market-day as I was going through Ballyseedy, Whom should I meet on the road but the Palatine's daughter? She asked me my name, "or where do you live? Will you come home with me for a while to my people's house?" I said, "I am a neat lad that lives in Currans".

2. "If you give up the Mass you will get me in marriage, As my friends have done, and all that are alive of them [i.e., of the Palatines]. You will get gold and silver and land rent-free with me, And a letter from Mr. Oliver [to say] that my father is old and past his work, And a pretty girl to go with you, if you fancy a Palatine."

3. I drew near her and gave her a couple of kisses. "And if I go home with you shall I get you in marriage?" She said, "Never fear, come with me and a thousand welcomes, And you will get me with my father's consent, and doubtless with my mother's too. You will get livestock on the land with me, and we shall live comfortably".

4. And now my little song is ended and there is neither pen nor ink in my hand. She took the fine young fellow home with her to her mother's. They completed the bargain and then he became the master. He got a house and land with her, and a snug, comfortable barn. And then he made a Catholic of the graceful gentle maid.

This is a County Kerry song, Ballyseedy being a short distance south-east of Tralee and Currans about half-way between Castleisland and Farranfore. "Mr. Oliver" was

69

doubtless a land-agent. As in the case of the preceding song, the English version is the production of some countryman, roughly translating the Irish.

The settlement of the Palatines in Munster forms an interesting story. The inhabitants of the Palatinate were reduced to penury by the War of the Spanish Succession, and the English Government of the day decided to plant some of them in Ireland with the idea of increasing the numerical strength of Protestantism in this country. The project was carried through at a cost of £20,000, borne by the Irish Exchequer, and in 1711 about three hundred families reached Dublin. Many of them remained there and quickly became absorbed in the general population. The rest settled on the land, mostly in Limerick and North Kerry, where the landlords leased holdings to them at a half or a third of the rent current in the district. "The poor Irish", says Arthur Young in his *Tour of Ireland*, "are seldom treated in this way. When they are, they work much greater improvements than is common among these Germans." About 1770 large numbers of them went to America, their departure being attributed by John Wesley to the selfish folly of the landlords, who exacted the full rent of the land as the leases fell in. Many of the remainder intermarried with the native Irish and became Catholics, like *The Palatine's Daughter*.

"CRABBED AGE AND YOUTH"

"Country marriage in Ireland follows an ancient and widespread pattern. It is called 'match-making' and it is the sort of *mariage de convenance* involving parental negotiations and a dowry which is nearly universal in Europe. In Ireland its importance is such as to make it the crucial point of rural social organization." So writes Dr. Conrad Arensberg in his invaluable anthropological study, *The Irish Countryman* (1937). He explains the system in detail and comments: "To our eyes, such a way of winning a wife seems very unromantic. It savours a little too much of hard-headed business. We should call a man a cynic who put farm and fortune ahead of personal attractions. Yet we should be wrong to make such an evaluation of the countryman. The sentiments prompting him, and his expectations, are quite different; they must be understood in their proper setting. In match-making, the interests of all the members of both families are deeply involved. The match is a convention by which they are expressed and realized. We are prone to forget that a living convention can be just as joyous, even more so, in fact, than bohemian revolt."

This is well said: and doubtless the great majority of these matches prove satisfactory from the point of view of marital happiness, at any rate after husband and wife have made the necessary self-adjustments. Also, an extreme disparity in age would be rare, the main object of the union being the perpetuation of the family. But during the eighteenth century (when the majority of our songs were made) cases did occur in which the parties were "misgraffèd in respect of years", the result being an "Auld Robin Gray" type of union which could not have been other than tragic. I give here two songs dealing with the marriage of young girls to old men, and the theme is treated in sublimated form in the celebrated eighteenth century poem *Cúirt an Mheadhon Oidhche* (*The Midnight Court*) by Brian Merriman, which has been published in more than one English translation.

SEANDUINE CHILL CHOCÁIN

THE OLD MAN OF KILCOCKAN

Moderato

Is teinn dúch an pós-a so, fó-ríor! a geall-adh dom, Go
By prayer and en-treat-y and threat they did wor-ry me To be

h-óg mé ceang-ail-the'g críon-don-án! Nuair a cuir-eadh le fór-sa 'n-a
wed to the gaf-fer my youth de-nied! On lead-en feet to the

chomhair go tigh'n tsag-airt me Im chroí bhí m'a-tuir-se'r linn é rá!
priest they did hur-ry me, With a heart stone-dead while the knot was tied.

Ní thaithn-eann a shiúl, a lúth ná a sheas-amh liom, A
I like not his gait, nor the rheum-y red eyes of him, His

mhal-a throm chlúmhach ná a shúil-e dear-ag-a, Go mb'fhearr liom óig-fhear a
fur-ry grey brows, the groans and the sighs of him, I long for a young man, to

phóg-fadh mo leac-a, Mo chroí gur cheang-ail san óg-bhuinn-eán!
lie and to rise with him, Who would kiss and car-ess me at morn-ing tide!

Is teinn dúch an pósa so, fó-ríor, a gealladh dom,
  Go h-óg mé ceangailthe 'g críon-donán!
Nuair a cuireadh le fórsa 'n-a chomhair go
  tigh an tsagairt me
Im chroí bhí m'atuirse ar linn é rá.
Ní thaithneann a shiúl, a lúth ná a sheasamh liom,
A mhala throm chlúmhach ná a shúile dearaga,
Go mb'fhearr liom óigfhear a phógfadh mo leaca,
  Mo chroí gur cheangail san óg-bhuinneán!

By prayer and entreaty and threat they did worry me
  To be wed to the gaffer my youth denied,
On leaden feet to the priest they did hurry me,
  With a heart stone dead while the knot was tied.
I like not his gait nor the rheumy red eyes of him,
His furry grey brows, the groans and the sighs
  of him,
I long for a young man, to lie and to rise with him,
  Who would kiss and caress me at morning-tide!

'S a chailíní óga, mo chomhairle má dheineann sibh,
  'S is teinn dúch atuirseach bhím dá bharr,
'S mé 'luí le seanduine caite gan luadar,
  'S ná fuil dá bharr agam ach uail bheag cnámha!
A' machtnamh a bhím san oíche ar mo leabaidh
Ar a' seanduine gcríonna, len' aois go gcrapann sé,
Seochas a' groí-fhear a shínfeadh ar leabaidh liom,
  'S go mb'fhiú é ar maidin a phóg úd 'fháil!

All maids yet unwed, whether wealthy or dowerless,
  Be warned by my fortune against old drones;
For I lie by a dotard both shrivelled and powerless,
  As good to possess as a heap of bones.
Wide-eyed each night, with a heart that's like lead in me,
I think of the withered old creature that's wed to me,
Compared to the stalwart that might lie abed with me,
  Clasping me to him with love's sweet tones!

Thúrfainn sé phíosa, 's é 'dhíol ar a' dtairrnge,
  D'éinne beó ghlacfadh mo sgéal 'n-a láimh,
Do luífeadh ar shúil mo sgrúile seanduine,
  Má thiocfadh a gan fhios i gcomhair é 'lámhach:
Chuirfeadh 'á bhátha é i lár na fairrge,
Shínfeadh sa' díg é 's a' claí do leaga air,
Nú cár bh'fhearr é mar ní ná an píop a chnaga dhe,
  'S mo sgrúile 'fháil marbh leath-uair roim lá?

Six guineas I'd give, and I'd pay it right readily,
  If someone would put my old man away,
Come on him by stealth and take aim at him steadily,
  Make sure of the target and earn his pay:
Or if in the sea he could set about drowning him,
Lay him flat in the ditch and knock the wall down on him,
Or perhaps better still just to throttle the jowl of him
  And leave him for dead just before the day!

73

Araoir ar mo leabaidh 's mé a' machtnamh trím
  néaltaibh,
 'Sea d'airíos gur cailleadh mo sheann-donán;
D'éiríos im sheasamh 's do ghabhas míle baochas
  Leis a' té úd a mhairbh sa' díg é ar lár.
'Sé airím 'á bhuachtaint gur shuathadar eatorrtha é
Gurbh í an láir rua do bhuail is do mhairbh é,
Beir sgéal leat uaim go dtí an buachaillín meacanta
  Gur chuireas mo sheanduine i gCill Chocáin!

Last night as I lay between waking and sleeping
  I heard that my wretched old man was dead;
I leapt from the pillow, my gratitude heaping
  On the man in the ditch who had done the deed.
They made up their story while still there was breath in him,
'Twas the bay mare that kicked him—and that was
    the death of him,
Go, take to the young man this news that is best for him—
  In the grave at Kilcockan my wretch is laid!

DONAL O'SULLIVAN

1. Weary and woeful, alas! is this wedding I was promised, To be tied in my youth to a withered old body; When I was forcibly sent to the priest's house to be married, My heart was full of grief while the words were being spoken. I don't like his walk, his movements or his postures, His heavy, furry brow or his red eyes; O! I would rather have a young man who would kiss my cheek, For my heart is set on a lusty youth!

2. Young girls, if you take my advice, And a sick, sorrowful, weary woman am I, Lying by a wasted, powerless old man, As good to possess as a little heap of bones. I think, as I lie in bed at night, Of the wasted old man, shrunk with age, Comparing him with the hearty fellow who might sleep by me, Whose kiss in the morning would be worth the getting!

3. I would give six guineas, and pay it on the nail, To anyone who would take my case in hand, Who would close (?) the eyes of my wretched old man, If he could catch him unawares and shoot him, Or put him to drown in the middle of the sea, Or stretch him out in the ditch and knock the wall down on him, Or why not rather just snap his neck, And find my old wretch dead half an hour before day?

4. Last night, as I lay between thinking and drowsing, I heard the old creature was dead. I rose up and poured forth my gratitude To him who had killed and felled him in the ditch. This is what I hear them determine upon, after discussing it, That it was the bay mare that had kicked and killed him. Go, take a message to the hearty lad from me, Tell him I have buried my old man in Kilcockan!

In his edition of the Kerry poet Diarmuid Ó Séaghdha (1937) my friend Seán Ó Súilleabháin includes a version of this song, noted from oral tradition. But the parish of Kilcockan is in County Waterford, on the river Blackwater about ten miles north of Youghal, a fact which renders a Kerry origin unlikely. The Kerry tradition is that the poem, or part of it, was intended as a joke. This may be so; but the verses are informed by such a passionate earnestness as almost to exclude the possibility of jest.

AN SEANDUINE   THE OLD MAN

Is triúr a bhí agam am cheangal le h-iarlais,
Mo mháthair is mh'athair is a' sagart chomh dian leó:
Chuadar abhaile 's do chaitheadar féasta,
'S is annamh a thigeann mo charaid 'om fhéachaint.

> *Is óró a sheanduine, leat-sa ní gheód-sa,*
> *Is óró a sheanduine, leat-sa ní gheód-sa,*
> *Oró a sheanduine, leat-sa ní gheód-sa,*
> *'S is mór a' trua an chríonnacht a' claoi leis*
>   *an óige!*

Comhairle 'sea fuaireas amuh ar a' mbóthar
O rógaire sagairt an seanduine 'phósa;
Ba chuma leis é ach go méadóinn a phócaí,
'S mé bheith fad a mhairfinn a' braith ar na comharsain.

Phós mise an seanduine, bhí orm díth-céille,
Rinne mé an méid sin ar chomhairle mo ghaolta;
Chuaidh mé abhaile leis—fó-ríor an sgéal san!
Is d'éirigh mé ar maidin is b'fhearr liom an t-éag dom.

There were three of them at me to wed the old gaffer,
My daddy, my mam—and the priest followed after;
Then they went home, a great feast they were spreading,
But my friends never see me now—after the wedding.

> *And O my old dotard, with you I'll not tarry,*
> *And O my old dotard, O why did I marry?*
> *Your body is shrivelled, your eye it is glassy,*
> *'Tis a plague when a withered man cleaves*
>   *to a lassie!*

The advice that I got while out walking the roadway
From a rogue of a priest was to marry the dotard.
'Twas little he cared, if well paid for his labours,
For the rest of my days I might look to the neighbours.

Deaved with their pleading I wed the old fellow,
Legs like two broomsticks, skin faded and yellow.
He took me off home—by my story take warning—
And I wished I was dead when I rose the next morning.

Dá bhfaghainn-se mo sheanduine báite i bpoll móna,
Thúrfainn abhaile é 's do dhéanfainn é 'thórramh,
Chuirfinn glas ar a' ndorus is an eochair im póca,
'S do shiúlóinn amach leis na buachaillíbh óga.

'S dá mbeadh súd agam-sa, capall is srian air,
Iallait mhaith leathair 'gus béalbhach iarainn,
Bhéarfainn mo sheanduine amach ins a' tsliabh liom,
'Gus do thúrfainn a' faraire abhaile ins an iallait.

Do chuas-sa go Corcaigh a d'iarraidh gléas tórraimh,
Tobac agus snaois agus cláracha cómhran:
Ar theacht dom abhaile go tuirseach tinn brónach,
Cé gheóinn ach mo sheanduine 'róstáil bruthóige!

Were he drowned in a bog-hole I'd readily take him
And carry him home, and right gladly I'd wake him.
I'd lock up the place to prevent any pillage,
And go for a stroll with the lads of the village.

If I had a horse and a saddle and bridle,
With reins and a bit, 'tisn't long I'd be idle.
I'd drive to the mountain and leave him there rotting,
And back with my lusty young sweetheart come trotting.

I went off to Cork to get whiskey to wake him,
Tobacco and snuff, and a coffin to make him.
I then started homeward and—as I'm a sinner—
There was my old man a-cooking his dinner!

DONAL O'SULLIVAN

1. There were three of them getting me married to an old wreck, My mother, my father, and the priest as keen as the others. They went home and enjoyed a feast, And seldom do my friends come to see me.
Chorus. And indeed, old man, I will not go with you, And 'tis a pitiful thing when age fastens on to youth!

2. I was counselled out on the road By a rogue of a priest to marry the old man. He cared nothing so long as I filled his pockets, Even though I should be depending on the neighbours for the rest of my days.

3. I wedded the old man, crazy as I was, And I did this on the advice of my kin. I went home with him—sorry the story! And when I rose in the morning I wished I was dead.

4. If I were to find my old man drowned in a bog-hole, I would bring him home and arrange a wake for him. I would lock the door and put the key in my pocket, And walk out with the young lads.

5. If I had these things, a horse with a bridle, A good leather saddle and an iron bit, I would take my old man out with me on the moor, And would bring home the lusty youth with me in the saddle.

6. I went to Cork to get materials for the wake, Tobacco and snuff and coffin-boards. When I reached home, woeful and weeping, Whom should I find but my old man roasting potatoes!

This song, part tragic, part grimly amusing, with a surprise in its last line, has sometimes been attributed to Andrew Magrath, the County Limerick poet who is the author of "Farewell to the Maigue" in the present volume (p. 93). It is reasonably certain, however, that the attribution is erroneous. It is an eighteenth century folk song of Munster origin, which has doubtless been subjected to many alterations and accretions, and versions of which have been noted as far away as County Mayo.

At the period of its composition, Scottish airs were very popular in Ireland, particularly with the Munster poets, and this song is said to have been written to the tune of "The Campbells Are Coming". It is interesting to note the profound modifications which the tune has undergone at the hands of the Irish folk singers.

LAMENTS

Irish elegiac verse might be divided broadly into two categories: the poems written by men of letters on the death of prominent or distinguished persons, and the folk poetry, generally of unknown authorship, which chronicles some fugitive, tragic event. Not unnaturally, it is in the latter rather than in the former that we must seek for the sincere expression of a grief genuinely felt.

Of the metres used for the formal elegies, that of the "Lament for Donough of Ballea" is perhaps the most common, and there are several tunes to which poems in this metre can be sung. The quaint tune to which Geoffrey O'Donoghue wrote his lament for his little dog would appear to have been used for lullabies as well as for laments.

There is no doubt that the author of a folk lament always had in mind a particular tune to which his composition was intended to be sung, and the metre he employed was conditioned by the structure of that tune. The variety of metres is much greater than in the case of the formal elegies; and the metre of some of them, such as "The Lone Rock", is somewhat involved.

It remains to refer to the laments used at wakes. Various attempts have been made, by Bunting, Petrie and others, to reduce to musical notation the wild and unrestrained ululations of the professional keening-women; but they were not very successful. The metrical form of the impromptu verses sometimes used on such occasions, and the type of tune that accompanied them, are well represented by "A Mock Lament".

CAOINE DHONNCHADHA BHAILE AODHA
LAMENT FOR DONOUGH OF BALLEA

Lento

Ó! os-na's éacht na h-Éir-eann tríd an dtreóir, Ó!
A sigh, a moan is heard through-out the land, A

Or-chra daor is créim d'fhuil Mhíl-eadh mhóir! Tor-char-tha tréith i
blow that strikes the Gaels on ev-'ry hand! The si-lent tomb en-

gcré 'n-a luí fé'n bhfód, Ó!___ Donn-ach-a tréan Bhail'
-clos-es___ Ire-land's best, Brave___ Don-ough of Bal-

Aodha, mo___mhíl-e___ brón! í ú í ú í ú.
-lea is___ laid to___ rest! ee oo ee oo ee oo.

Osna agus éacht na h-Éireann tríd an dtreóir,	A sigh, a moan is heard throughout the land,
Orchra daor is créim d'fhuil Mhíleadh mhóir!	A blow that strikes the Gaels on every hand!
Torchartha tréith i gcré 'n-a luí fén bhfód,	The silent tomb encloses Ireland's best,
Donncha tréan Bhaile Aodha, mo mhíle brón!	Brave Donough of Ballea is laid to rest!
Is brón 's is cumha trí Mhúsgraí trasna go préimh	The rest of Ireland shares in Muskerry's woe,
Stór na ndúithchí i gclúid fí leacaibh go faon;	In grief so great a chief is thus laid low;
Pór na bprionnsaí d'úr-chraoibh Chaisil na récs,	A scion he of Cashel's kings and lords,
I ngleó nár bh'ionntaoibh ionnsaí a phearsan le faor.	His honour aye unsullied as his sword's.
Faor is fuiling is fuinneamh is fíoch nár thláth,	Swordsmanship, endurance, courtesy,
Tréin-neart cuisleann is mire nár claoidheadh go bás,	These were the hero's gifts for all to see,
Féile, cumann is tuigsint le linn an gháidh:	With timely help to all that stood in need,
Sin tréithe an bhile, 's mo mhille-sa a ghníomhartha ar lár!	To every such a tower of strength indeed!
I lár a mhaitheasa is mairg do chaill an triath,	In deed and word he proved until the end
Ráib na gaisge, an faraire feidhm-ghlic fial,	Good host, wise mentor, counsellor and friend,
Nár fhág a charaid ar thearmonn cladhaire riamh	Who ne'er would let a tyrant's power prevail
I sráid, i gcathair, ná i gcarcair fé ghreim gan riar.	In town or country, citadel or gaol.

SEÁN Ó MURCHADHA NA RÁITHÍNEACH   DONAL O'SULLIVAN

1. A sigh and a moan throughout the whole course of Ireland, A grievous blow and a gnawing pain to the great Milesian blood! Laid low in the clay, lying under the sod, Brave Donough of Ballea, my thousand sorrows!

2. Sorrow and grief through the breadth of Muskerry to its depths, The country's treasure covered over, prostrate in a tomb, The seed of the princes of the noble branch of Cashel of the kings, In combat no one would venture to attack his person with a sword.

3. Swordsmanship, endurance, vigour and wrath not weak, Strength of arm and agility never overcome till death, Generosity, affection and understanding in time of need, These were the hero's traits—alas! that his activities are at an end!

4. It is a pity that we have lost the chieftain at the height of his goodness, The champion of valour, the deed-clever, generous one, Who left not ever his friends in the power of a villain, In a street, in a city, or in prison in an unyielding grip.

This elegy is one of the usual type written by the eighteenth century poets for members of the Irish aristocracy of the period. Its subject is Donough (or Denis) MacCarthy of

Ballea Castle, near Carrigaline in the barony of Muskerry, County Cork, and about eight miles south-east of Cork City. MacCarthy, many of whose ancestors had been kings of Cashel, died on the 2nd April, 1739, at the age of forty-five and was buried with his forbears on the north side of the high altar in the Franciscan Abbey of Kilcrea, founded in 1478. Tradition has it that he was a man of giant stature and a master in the use of the short sword—facts which are perhaps alluded to in the third verse.

The author of the poem, Seán Ó Murchadha na Ráithíneach (John Murphy of Raheen) was born at Carrignavar, County Cork, in 1700 and died in 1762. A poet in the learned tradition of his time, he wrote a varied amount of verse (including religious verse) but is chiefly known for his elegiac compositions. The present lament runs to fifteen quatrains, and it will be noticed that it is written in chain-verse (Irish *conchlann*): that is to say, the final word of each quatrain is the first word of the one which follows.

The poem is in literary Irish, which is as far removed from the language of ordinary conversation as the English of Pope or Dryden is from current speech. Yet it was sung for Dr. Joyce in 1851 by a simple farm labourer, Phil Gleeson, of Coolfree, Ballyorgan, County Limerick. The explanation is that, despite the Penal Laws, the traditional love of learning lingered on, fostered by that admirable body of nomadic teachers known as the hedge-school masters.

Gleeson's traditional manner of singing this elegy (which of course he learnt from older people) is given by Joyce as follows: "To the note B at the end of the air he chanted, in monotone, a sort of *crónán* (crooning) consisting simply of the continued repetition of the two vowel sounds, *ee–oo*, *ee–oo*, *ee–oo*, etc., which was prolonged *ad libitum*: the change from *ee* to *oo* being made at intervals of about a crotchet. Occasionally he ended the *crónán* by suddenly sliding his voice up to the third, fifth or octave—a common practice in laments, nurse tunes, plough whistles, etc." There are similar instances in the Milking Song and the Plough Song contained in the present volume (pp. 33, 37).

DRUIMÍN

DRIMEEN

Is brón-ach mo— thocht, Go tóir-seach dom shlad, Is
There's a catch in my— throat As I view the sad scene, I

cró-lag mo chorp, Is deór-ach mo dhearc.— Ím- bó— 'gus um- bó.
mourn for my doat, My dar-ling Drim-een.— Eem- bo— and um- bo.

Is brónach mo thocht,
  Go tóirseach dom shlad,
Is crólag mo chorp,
  Is deórach mo dhearc.

I sgeólaibh na sgol,
  I seódaibh na sean,
I gceóltaibh na gcrot,
  Is ró-bheag mo ghean.

Mo choileán dob óg,
  Is díombádhach a chríoch,
Cé'r ghiobanta a ghlór,
  Níor dhíoghbháil a ghníomh.

A thuitim le luich
  Is miste mo rath,
Dob fhusaide a dhul
  Dá dtuitfeadh le cat.

Dob uallach a chor
  A' sguaba na sgart,
A' ruaga na lon
  As bhruachaibh a nead.

I ndoiríbh an Ruis
  Ná i gCuimín na gCros
Ní imínn im chuis
  Gan Druimín lem chois.

An tan luínn ar mo leis,
  Do shíneadh lem ais,
A dhlaoithe dom dheis
  Do chíorainn lem bais.

Do shleamhnuigh an luch
  'N-a dhranndal isteach
(Ba gheanncach a smulc)
  I dteannta ag an gcat.

Mo lurán gur éag
  Níor speadán i spórt,
Mo leannán mo léan,
  Mo bheagán mo bhrón.

SÉAFRADH Ó DONNCHADHA AN GHLEANNA

There's a catch in my throat
  As I view the sad scene,
I mourn for my doat,
  My darling Drimeen.

For the things of the mind,
  For music and such,
I'm no longer inclined—
  I miss him too much.

My poor little dog,
  How unhappy his end!
Though his bark might be fierce,
  He was everyone's friend.

And to die through a mouse!
  I am heavy for that!
Better woodcock or grouse,
  Or even a rat!

To poke in the bushes
  Was what he loved best,
A-scaring the thrushes
  From out of their nest.

In the woodlands of Ross,
  By the shores of Lough Leane,
I was ne'er at a loss—
  There was always Drimeen!

Right well we'd agree
  As I lay in my chair,
His head on my knee
  And my hand in his hair!

But mousie slipped out,
  And he choked poor Drimeen;
No wonder—his snout
  Was the biggest yet seen.

So my dear little pet
  Has drawn his last breath;
I grieve for him yet,
  And I'll miss him till death!

DONAL O'SULLIVAN

1. There is a catch in my throat That oppresses me sadly, My body is enfeebled, My eyes are tearful.
2. In the tales of the schools, In the jewels of eld, In the music of harps, Small is my interest.
3. My young little puppy, Pitiful is his end. Though his bark was snappish, He never did any harm.
4. His being killed by a mouse Was worse luck for me. I had borne it more easily If he had fallen through a cat.
5. Proud was his action As he searched the bushes, Chasing the blackbirds From the edge of their nests.

6. In the woods of Ross, Or at Kilcummin of the Crosses, I would not go walking Without Drimeen beside me.

7. When I reclined on my hip, He would lie at my feet, His hair at my right hand, I used to stroke it with my palm.

8. The mouse slipped Into his throat (Its snout was snub-nosed), When cornered by the cat.

9. My pet has died Who was no laggard in sport. I grieve for my darling, I sorrow for my little one.

Geoffrey O'Donoghue, the author of this charming piece, was a cultured aristocrat impoverished by the Cromwellian wars. He was Chief of his sept and lived in the storied castle of Killaha at the entrance to Glenflesk, County Kerry, whence he took his title of O'Donoghue of the Glen. The scenery hereabouts—mountain and lake, river and woodland—is of incomparable beauty. The river Flesk runs through the glen, past the ruined castle and into Lough Leane, which is the lower lake of Killarney. Ross Castle, anciently a stronghold of the O'Donoghues, stands on the shore of the lake. Drimeen was the poet's pet spaniel. He and the cat were in the barn together, chasing the mice while a corn-stack was being re-made. An outsize mouse, in endeavouring to escape from the cat, jumped into Drimeen's mouth and choked him to death.

In its sentiments and in the short lines of its versification, this tender threnody recalls the poem on his dog Peloton written upwards of a century earlier by the Renaissance poet Joachim du Bellay, whom Geoffrey O'Donoghue resembles in his breeding, his scholarship and his leisured poverty. It could be said of the one, as Hilaire Belloc wrote of the other, that "a lightness almost sardonic lay above the depths of his grief, and the tenderness which attached to his home played around the things that go with quietude—his books and animals." A few lines from du Bellay's elegy should illustrate the point:

> Peloton ne caressoit,
> Sinon ceulx qu'il cognoissoit,
> Et n'eust pas voulu repaistre
> D'autre main que de son maistre,
> Qu'il alloit tousjours suyvant:
> Quelquefois marchoit devant,
> Faisant ne sçay quelle feste
> D'un gay branlement de teste.

CARRAIG AONAIR   THE LONE ROCK

Ó! Luan dubh an áir tháinig suaineas ró-bhreá,
On that Mon-day of woe far a-way you did row, Do
ghluais-iú-ir uaim-se leath-uair-ín roim lá,
peace-ful the sea was an hour ere dawn's glow. Ag
ias-gach ar bhád i gcian-taibh d'úr mbá,
lit-tle did know that cold death hov-ered low, That
iar-sma na blia-na 's 'n-úr ndiaidh go bhfaghad bás.
sad day still haunts me wher-ev-er I go.

Ó! Luan dubh an áir tháinig suaineas ró-bhreá,
Do ghluaisiúir uaim-se leath-uairín roim lá
Ag iasgach ar bhád i gciantaibh d'úr mbá,
D'fhonn iarsma na bliana 's 'n-úr ndiaidh go
     bhfaghad bás.

'Sé Domhnall mo mhaoin an té b'óige dem chloinn,
'Gus caoicíos ón lá san 'sea tháini' sé i dtír,
Gan tapa, gan bhrí, gan anam 'n-a chroí,
Ach a ghéaga boga geala 's iad leathta ar a' dtuinn.

'Sé Tomás mo stór, rogha na bhfear óg,
Bhí modhamhail maiseach múinte, géar-chumtha
       go leór.
Leis an mbúcla bhí 'n-a bhróig do sgrí sé ar a' gcóir
Gurab í Carraig Aonair a chéile go deó.

Is tá duine eile 'em chloinn nár thráchtas air puinn,
Cormac, mo chogarach, ceann cothuithe mo thighe,
Thugadh an fia leis ón gcoill is an bradán ón linn,
Feadóga dubha an tsléi 'ge 's gan bhréig cearca
       fraoigh.

'Sí an Nodlaig seo chúinn an Nodlaig gan fonn
Dom cheathrar breá brolla'-gheal fé shruthaibh
       na dtonn.
Dá dtigidís chúm tá go doimhin ins a' tsrúill,
Is breá dhéanfainn iad do chaoine is do shíne i
       n-Achadh Dúin.

'Sé mo chreach is mo dhíth nár leigeas iad ar luing
I gcomhar le Saoi Séamus mar a dtéadh na
     Wild Geese:
Bheadh mo shúil-se le Críost le n-a gcumann arís,
Is nárbh í Carraig Aonair ba chéile dhom chloinn.

On that Monday of woe far away you did row,
Calm and peaceful the sea was an hour ere dawn's
       glow.
Ah! you little did know that cold death hovered low—
That sad day still haunts me wherever I go.

Young Donal, ah! he was the babe of the three,
Two weeks from their sailing he came back to me;
With the wind on the lee and the waves running free,
A pale lifeless corpse he returned from the sea.

And Thomas, he too has left me to rue,
So handsome, so sturdy, a man through and
       through.
With the hasp of his shoe he wrote out the clue,
That the Lone Rock had claimed him her lover to woo.

Lastly Cormac, my pet, I've not mentioned him yet,
A comelier huntsman no man ever met.
The best salmon he'd net, the best woodcock
       he'd get,
In the pools, on the hills, in fair weather and wet.

This coming Yule-tide all joy is denied
To my white-breasted boys that lie under the tide.
Were they with me who died, I would keen them
       with pride,
And in Aghadown I'd lay them in the grave, side
       by side.

My grey hairs would have ease had I granted their pleas
To take ship with Sir James and to join the
     Wild Geese.
But there's now no release from this grief without cease,
And the Lone Rock for ever is wedded to these.

Mo chreach is mo chás ná deachúir don Spáinn,
Nó i gcongnamh leis an bhFranncach 'déanamh
    aimhlis bhur námhad,
Ó chonnac an lá a ndeachúir bhur mbá,
Gan coinne len bhur gcongnamh ná tnúth go
    bhfaghainn bás.

A 'nighean Ó mo chroí, ná goil-se 's ná caoi,
Mar gheó tú togha nóchair dhéanfaidh romhar
    dhuit is crích.
Ní bhfaghad-sa mo bhuíon ná mo thriúr
    d'fearaibh ghrinn,
Ná mo cheathrar breá múinte de lúbairíbh groí.

A chlann Ó mo chroí, nó an trua libh mar a bhím,
Bhur n-athair bocht in' aonar a' géar-ghol 's a' caoi?
'N-a chuaile throm chríon i gcúil uaigneach a' tighe,
Is an bhean atá i n-áit bhur máthar ní cás lé mar
    bhím.

Ar mo ghlúinibh nuair théim isteach chun tighe Dé,
Is fhéachaim ar an gcúinne a mbíodh mo thriúr
    ann a' léamh,
Tagann greim in mo thaobh ná leigheasfar lem ré,
'S a Dhia mhóir! nach trua mé 's gan fuasgla
    ar mo phéin!

Nuair théim ar an gclaí is d'fhéachaim uaim síos,
Nuair chím Carraig Aonair, Ó pléasgann mo chroí.
Thar n'ais dhom arís go mullach mo thighe,
'Gus is í Carraig Aonair is céile dhom chloinn.

CONCHUBHAR Ó LAOGHAIRE

I recall you were fain to cross over to Spain,
In the ranks of King Louis our freedom
    to gain,
But my woe and my bane! you lie deep in the main,
Your drowned faces deny me all surcease
    of pain.

My poor daughter! don't weep! If he's lost on the deep,
You may still wed another who will sow for you
    and reap.
For me—lonely I creep, and my vigil I keep,
My strong-armed young stalwarts come between
    me and sleep.

My dead sons! do you know the depth of my woe,
As withered and gaunt through the household I go?
Sad and sadder I grow as I pace to and fro,
While your step-mother cares not what's grieving
    me so.

When to God's house I steal my frenzy to heal,
And my eyes meet the spot where my boys used
    to kneel,
Like salmon in creel I shiver and reel,
Great God! must I suffer the torment
    I feel?

When I climb the hill side and the sea-opens wide,
And I view the Lone Rock, ' tis as if I had died.
Back at home as I bide my tears flow like a tide,
And the Lone Rock eternal remains my sons' bride.

DONAL O'SULLIVAN

1. On that fatal Monday there came a deceptive calm, And you went from me a short half-hour before daybreak, To go fishing in a boat and to be drowned far away, To get a New Year's gift [of fish], and I shall die after your loss.

2. Donal, my beloved, was the youngest of my children, And it was a fortnight from that day that he came ashore, Without strength or vigour, without life in his heart, But with his soft white limbs spread on the waves.

3. Thomas was my treasure, the flower of young men, Mannerly and handsome he was, well-bred, beautifully built. With the buckle of his shoe he wrote on the rudder That the Lone Rock would be his spouse for ever.

4. And there is another of my children I have not mentioned yet, Cormac, my darling, the prop of my household. He would bring the deer from the wood, and the salmon from the pool, Black mountain plover and grouse as well.

5. This coming Christmas will be a joyless Christmas For my four, fair, white-breasted ones under the tide. Could they but return to me who are deep in the sea, Well would I keen them and lay them in Aghadown!

6. Ah! woe is me that I did not let them go aboard ship Along with Sir James in the wake of the Wild Geese! Then I should have hoped in Christ for their society again, And that the Lone Rock would not be my children's spouse.

7. 'Tis a thousand pities you did not go to Spain, Or to help the French and to spoil your foes, Since I have seen the day when you went away to be drowned, And I cannot look for your help, or hope to die.

8. My beloved daughter, do not weep, do not grieve, For you will get a choice husband who will dig for you and maintain you. I shall not get my company, nor my three joyous lads, Nor my fine, well-bred quartet of strong stalwarts.

9. My darling children, do you not pity me, Your poor lonely father weeping and crying? A heavy, withered, gaunt man in a lonely corner of the house, While the woman who has your mother's place is untouched by my suffering.

10. When I enter the house of God and kneel down, And look at the corner where my three sons used to read [their prayers], There comes into my breast a pain that will never be cured. Great God! am I not to be pitied in my helpless torment?

11. When I climb on the ditch and look downwards, When I see the Lone Rock my heart bursts. Back I go again to the top of my house, And it is the Lone Rock that is my children's spouse.

84

This poignant lament was composed by a native of south-west Cork for his three sons and a son-in-law, drowned at sea. They went fishing a few days before Christmas and were wrecked on Carraig Aonair ("The Lone Rock"). This rock is situated four and a half miles south-west of Cape Clear, the most southerly point of Ireland. The Fastnet Lighthouse, first built on the rock in 1853, is a familiar object to voyagers to and from the United States. The four young men managed to scramble to temporary safety, and before being overcome by the rising tide one of the sons scratched a last message on the rudder of the wrecked boat with the buckle of his shoe, to tell what their fate had been. The son-in-law is not mentioned by name, but he is alluded to in verse 8. Aghadown, where the father wished his boys to be buried, is on the mainland, opposite Clear Island.

As is well known, "The Wild Geese" was the name given to those Irish soldiers who left Ireland after the Capitulation of Limerick in 1691 and took service in the armies of the Continent. If the victims of the tragedy had been in a position to join them, as the poem suggests, it must have been composed not long after their departure; and for this reason it is the more noteworthy that the name "Wild Geese" is given in English. "*Na Géadhna Fiadhaine*", which is the Irish equivalent, is frequently seen since the Irish language revival movement began in modern times; but there is no evidence that the Wild Geese were so called by their contemporaries.

The Sir James mentioned in the sixth verse may be Sir James FitzEdmund Cotter, of Baile na Speire (Anngrove), near Carrigtuohill, County Cork. Sir James was a distinguished adherent of the Stuarts and slew the regicide John Lisle at Lausanne in 1664. King James appointed him Governor of the City of Cork "and the Great Island near it" (Cove) in February, 1690; and during the wars of 1690–1691 he commanded for the King in Munster until the Capitulation.

The name of the author of the lament is remembered traditionally in Clear Island as Conchubhar Ó Laoghaire (Conor O'Leary). It is worthy to be chronicled here as that of a true poet. On the other hand, Crofton Croker took down a version of which he published a translation (but not, unfortunately, the original) in his *Researches in the South of Ireland* (1824), p. 175; and he there gives the name as O'Donoghue.

CAOINE MAGAIDH

MOCK LAMENT

Andante

Ó!____ mol - a mór le Muir - e, Mar tá clia-thán mo thighe—se
I____ praise the Vir - gin Ma - ry, That my house is sound and

clu - thar, 'Gus cruach mhón im chis-tin, Is m'fhear tighe a'
air - y, With turf heaped by____ the way-side, And my man____ bound

dul____ 'on roil - ig,____ A____ Sheáin óig, a riúin!
for____ the grave-side,____ My____ Shawn ogue, a - roon!

REFRAIN

A____ Sheáin,____ trí lár____ mo chroí a-nonn! Do chos - a fad - a
O____ Shawn,____ it breaks my heart full soon! Your spind - ly yel - low

buí____ Sín - te síos le taobh do thighe, ____ A
legs____ Stretched out like wood - en pegs, ____ O

Sheái - ái - ái - ái - ái - áin, trí lár____ mo____ chroí a - nonn!
Shaw - aw - aw - aw-aw-awn, it breaks my____ heart full soon!

LAMENTATION
Poco più mosso

Gol a gol __ ó, gol ó, gol ó, ____ Gol ó gol ó, gol
Gul a gul - o, gul o, gul o, ____ Gul o gul o, gul

ó, ____ gol ó, ____ gol; Gol a gol __ ó, gol
o, ____ gul o, ____ gul; Gul a gul __ o, gul

ó, gol ó, ____ A Sheáin, trí lár____ mo____ chroí a - nonn! ____
o, gul o, ____ O Shawn, it breaks my____ heart full soon! ____

Ó! mola mór le Muire,
Mar tá cliathán mo thighe-se cluthar,
'Gus cruach mhón' im chistin,
Is m'fhear tighe a' dul 'on roilig,
    A Sheáin óig, a riúin!

I praise the Virgin Mary
That my house is sound and airy,
With turf heaped by the wayside,
And my man bound for the graveside,
    My Shawn ogue aroon!

A Sheáin, trí lár mo chroí anonn!
  Do chosa fada buí
  Sínte síos le taobh do thighe,
A Sheáin, trí lár mo chroí anonn!

  Gol a gol ó, gol ó, gol ó,
  Gol ó, gol ó, gol ó, gol ó, gol;
  Gol a gol ó, gol ó, gol ó,
    A Sheáin, trí lár mo chroí anonn!

Mo thaisge is mo riún tú!
Is do bhuailthá mé le craobh is rúta,
Is le ceann reamhar a',tsúiste;
Is mola bhéarfad 'on Ur-Mhac
Mar ba dhuit-se ba thúisge,
  A Sheáin óig, a riúin!

Mo ghrá tú is mo thaisge!
Do thugthá dhom an taobh ba chrua den leabain,
An chuid ba chaoile 'en bheatha,
'S an ceann ba raimhre 'en bhata,
  A Sheáin óig, a riúin!

Mo ghrá tú is mo chumann!
Do chuirthá na cearca chun nide,
Do thógthá an t-ím den chuiginn,
Is mise sa' chúinne a' sile,
  A Sheáin óig, a riúin!

Mo ghrá tú is mo chiall!
'S tá féasóg ar do ghiall,
Gan tú a' féachaint soir ná siar,
Is t'anam gléigeal ag an ndial,
  A Sheáin óig, a riúin!

Mo chreach mór is mo lat!
Nuair a gheóir-se uaim amach
Is baralín bán id ghlaic,
Is tairnge síos id chab,
Do chualacht suas let ais,
Is mise rómpa amach,
Mo ramhan agam 's mo shluasad
Chun clúdaithe anuas ort,
  A Sheáin óig, a riúin!

Cuirfead leac le cúl do chinn,
Is leac eile le trácht do bhuinn,
Dhá leac dhéag nó trí
Anuas ar aghaidh do chroí
Ná leigfidh duit éirghe aníos,
  A Sheáin óig, a riúin!

Ach ní chreidfinn féin ón ríocht
Ná go bpreabfá fós it shuí
'S bheadh bata glas ón gcoill
Go h'árd ós cionn mo chinn,
  A Sheáin óig, a riúin!

O Shawn, it breaks my heart full soon!
  Your spindly, yellow legs
  Stretched out like wooden pegs,
O Shawn, it breaks my heart full soon!

  Gul a gul O, gul O, gul O,
  Gul O, gul O, gul O, gul O, gul;
  Gul a gul O, gul O, gul O,
    O Shawn, it breaks my heart full soon!

My darling and my treasure!
To me you gave full measure
Of beatings and of thumpings!
Thank God all that is o'er me,
That He took you before me,
  My Shawn ogue aroon!

Alas, you lie so still O!
You gave *me* the hardest pillow,
The smallest bit for eating,
The biggest stick for beating,
  My Shawn ogue aroon!

My love, my sweet, my pet!
You'd care for ducks and chickens,
But you took all the pickings,
And left me weeping yet,
  My Shawn ogue aroon!

My sweetheart so forlorn!
Your jowl is all unshorn,
Your eyes are wide and staring,
'Tis not to heaven you're faring,
  My Shawn ogue aroon!

My woe! my bitter grieving!
When now I see you leaving,
Clutching your white shroud,
And followed by the crowd,
The mourners with the pall,
Myself in front of all,
Equipped with spade and shovel
To heap the earth and rubble
  On Shawn ogue aroon!

At your head a stone I'll put,
Another at the foot,
Twelve stones, perhaps thirteen,
I'll space them in between,
To make sure you've taken root,
  My Shawn ogue aroon!

But somehow still I fear me
One day you'll jump out near me,
From out the churchyard hasting,
And then I'll get a basting
  From Shawn ogue aroon!

DONAL O'SULLIVAN

1. Great praise be to [the Virgin] Mary That I have a house with sound walls, And a heap of turf in my kitchen, And my man going to the churchyard, Johnny, my love!
   Chorus. Johnny, [it goes] right through my heart! Your long yellow legs Stretched along the side of your house, Johnny, [it goes] right through my heart! Woe, woe, etc., Johnny, [it goes] right through my heart!
   2. My treasure and my darling! You used to club me with branch and root, And with the stout end of the flail; And I will praise the Noble Son That you were the first to go, Johnny, my love!

3. My love and my treasure! You used to give me the hardest side of the bed, And the smallest portion of food, And the biggest end of the stick, Johnny, my love!

4. My love and my dear! You used to put the hens to nest, And take the butter from the churn, While I was crying in the corner, Johnny, my love!

5. My love and my sweetheart! There is a beard on your jaw, And you are looking neither this way nor that, And your bright soul is with the devil, Johnny, my love!

6. O grief and desolation! When you leave me and go out, Clutching your white shroud, With a nail down through your gob, The company walking beside you, And myself in front of them all, Carrying my spade and shovel To cover you up with, Johnny, my love!

7. I shall put a stone at the back of your head, And another at the soles of your feet, And twelve stones or thirteen Right over your heart, So that you cannot rise up again, Johnny, my love!

8. Yet nothing shall persuade me That you will not jump up some day, And brandish a green stick from the wood High over my head, Johnny, my love!

The story that goes with this West Kerry lament is that it was composed by a woman whose husband pretended to be dead so that he might hear the kind of character she would give him at his wake. He must have been considerably mortified—especially when, on reaching the *olagón* or lamentation, she rendered it as a song of joy, dancing the while!

It is interesting to recall that this is the theme on which J. M. Synge, who was familiar with West Kerry, based his play *The Shadow of the Glen*. In the last verse of the song "The Old Man" in the present volume (p. 75) the supposedly dead husband also proves to be alive.

The tune must be considerably older than the words and it was doubtless used for serious laments in the same metre, several of which are extant. The strophic form of the verses lends itself peculiarly to extempore composition, such as was common at wakes. Usually, the opening line of each verse apostrophizes the deceased in affectionate terms, and the assonance of this line determines that of the succeeding lines in the same verse.

The verses being of varying length, some explanation of the manner of singing them is called for. The last three lines of each verse are sung as the last three lines of verse one, and the opening strain is repeated as often as is required until the third line from the end is reached.

SONGS OF REMEMBRANCE
AND FAREWELL

We have in Ireland an unusual number of songs in which the writers bid a loving farewell to the place where their heart is, or, if already removed from it, remember it with affection.   With the exception of the first piece in the present section, these songs do not envisage Ireland as a whole, but some particular place, the scene of the poet's boyhood or of his happier years.

He may be a friar, transferred from his beloved abbey under the shadow of Croagh-patrick, which he says he would never have left but for his vow of obedience; or a young ecclesiastical student forced by the Penal Laws to pursue his studies on the Continent, far from the Tipperary glen where he swam and sported and played; or a Mayo man living in Munster who begs the wind to waft a kiss to the place of his affections, much like the love-lorn girl in "The Braes o' Yarrow":

> O gentle wind that bloweth south
>   From where my love repaireth,
> Convey a kiss from his sweet mouth
>   And tell me how he fareth;

or a poet forced by circumstances to forsake his favourite haunt.   But, whatever the author, there runs through all these verses a monotone of sadness which is the sincere expression of a nostalgic longing:

> I cannot but remember such things were
> That were most precious to me.

Poco sostenuto

Beir— bean - nacht óm chroí go — tír na — h-Éir - eann,
Take a bless-ing from my heart to the land of my birth, And the

Bán - chnuic Éir - eann Ó! Chun a mair - eann de shíol - ra —
fair — hills of Éir - e — O! And to all that sur-vive of—

Ír is — Éibh - ir Ar bhán - chnuic Éir - eann — Ó!
Éibh-ear's tribe on earth On the fair — hills of Éir - e — O!

An — áit — úd 'n-ar bh'aoibh - inn — binn — ghuth éan Mar —
In that land — so de - light - ful the wild thrush's lay Seems to

shámh - chruit chaoin a' — caoin - e — Gaodhal; 'Sé mo chás — bheith míl - e —
pour a la-ment forth for Éir - e's de-cay; A - las, a - las, why pine — I a

míl' i — gcéin Ó — bhán - chnuic Éir - eann Ó!
thous-and miles a - way From the fair — hills of Éir - e — O!

Beir beannacht óm chroí go tír na h-Éireann,
　Bán-chnuic Éireann Ó!
Chun a maireann de shíolra Ír is Éibhir
　Ar bhán-chnuic Éireann Ó!
An áit úd 'n-ar bh'aoibhinn binn-ghuth éan
Mar shámh-chruit chaoin a' caoine Gaodhal;
'Sé mo chás bheith míle míl' i gcéin
　Ó bhán-chnuic Éireann Ó!

Bíonn barr bog slím ar chaoin-chnuic Éireann,
　Bán-chnuic Éireann Ó!
'S is fearr ná'n tír seo díogha gach sléibh' ann,
　Bán-chnuic Éireann Ó!
Dob árd a coillte 's ba dhíreach réidh,
'S a mbláth mar aol ar mhaoilinn géag,
Tá grá am chroí im inntinn féin
　Do bhán-chnuic Éireann Ó!

Is osgailte fáilteach an áit sin Éire,
　Bán-chnuic Éireann Ó!
'Gus tora na sláinte i mbarr na déise
　I mbán-chnuic Éireann Ó!
Ba bhinne ná méar' ar théadaibh ceóil
Seinm is géimre a laogh 's a mbó
Agus taithneamh na gréine orra, aosda 's óg,
　Ar bhán-chnuic Éireann Ó!

DONNCHA RUA MAC CON MARA

Take a blessing from my heart to the land of my birth,
　And the fair hills of Éire O!
And to all that survive of Éibhear's tribe on earth
　On the fair hills of Éire O!
In that land so delightful the wild thrush's lay
Seems to pour a lament forth for Éire's decay;
Alas! alas! why pine I a thousand miles away
　From the fair hills of Éire O!

The soil is rich and soft, the air is mild and bland
　Of the fair hills of Éire O!
Her barest rock is greener to me than this rude land—
　O! the fair hills of Éire O!
Her woods are tall and straight, grove rising over grove,
Trees flourish in her glens below and on her heights above.
O! in heart and in soul I shall ever, ever love
　The fair hills of Éire O!

A fruitful clime is Éire's, through valley, meadow, plain,
　And the fair hills of Éire O!
The very bread of life is in the yellow grain
　On the fair hills of Éire O!
Far dearer unto me than the tones music yields
Is the lowing of the kine and the calves in her fields,
And the sunlight that shone long ago on Gaelic shields
　On the fair hills of Éire O!

JAMES CLARENCE MANGAN

91

1. Take a blessing from my heart to the land of Ireland, The fair hills of Ireland O! To the descendants of Íor and Éibhear that abide On the fair hills of Ireland O! Delightful in that spot was the sweet song of birds, Like a soothing, gentle harp lamenting the Gaels. It is my sorrow that I am a thousand miles distant From the fair hills of Ireland O!

2. Smooth and soft are the summits of the gentle Irish hills, The fair hills of Ireland O! And the bareness of every mountain is preferable to this country, The fair hills of Ireland O! High are her forests, straight and level, With flowers lime-white a-top of the branches. I have love in my heart in my own mind For the fair hills of Ireland O!

3. A place open and hospitable is Ireland, The fair hills of Ireland O! And the fruit of health is in the tops of the ears of corn On the fair hills of Ireland O! Sweeter-sounding than fingers on music's strings Are the calling and lowing of her calves and their cows, And the sunlight on them, old and young, On the fair hills of Ireland O!

Though this song is usually attributed to the eighteenth century poet Donncha Rua Mac Con Mara or Macnamara, it is probable that he did little more than revise, and add to, an earlier song by an Irish soldier named Fitzgerald, who was a major in the French army at the storming of the Dutch fortress of Bergen-op-Zoom, 16th September, 1748.

Macnamara, usually called Donncha Rua (Red-haired Denis), was born at Cratloe, County Clare, in 1715 and probably received his education in Limerick City. About 1740, the Year of the Great Frost, he arrived in County Waterford, where he earned his living as an assistant schoolmaster. Somewhere in the decade beginning 1745 he went to Newfoundland, and as this was the only occasion when he was absent from Ireland it seems likely that the song in its present form was written then. The Irish for Newfoundland is *Talamh an Éisc* ("Land of the Fish"), and in those days the fishermen of Waterford and others of our south coast ports regularly made the trip to the Grand Banks for the cod-fishing—just as the fishermen of Lisbon do to-day.

Returned from abroad, Macnamara fell upon evil days. He became a Protestant for a time, with a view to bettering his condition, but reverted to the old faith before his death in 1810. He is buried in Newtown, near Kilmacthomas, County Waterford.

Íor and Éibhear, mentioned in the first verse of the song, were sons of Mílidh (Milesius). They are the supposed ancestors of the Gaels, who were known to the genealogists as Clanna Míleadh (Milesians).

SLÁN LE MÁIGH

FAREWELL TO THE MAIGUE

Andante

Ó! ___ slán ___ is ___ céad ón ___ dtaobh so ___ uaim Cois ___
A ___ long ___ fare - well I ___ send to ___ thee, Fair ___

Máighe na ___ gcaor, na ___ gcraobh, na ___ gcruach, Na stáid, na ___ séad, na ___
Maigue of ___ corn and ___ fruit and ___ tree, Of state and ___ gift and ___

saor, na ___ slua, Na ___ ndán, na ndréacht, na ___ dtréan gan ___ ghruaim!
gath - 'ring ___ grand, Of ___ song, ro - mance and ___ chief - tain ___ bland!

CHORUS

Is ___ och, och - ón! is ___ breóit - e ___ mis - e, Gan
And ___ och, och - one! dark ___ for - tune's ___ rig - our, Wealth,

chuid, gan chóir, gan ___ chóip, gan ___ chis - de, Gan sult, gan seód, gan ___
ti - tle, ___ tribe of ___ glor - ious ___ fig - ure, Feast, gift — all gone, and ___

spórt, gan ___ spion - na, Ó seól - adh me chun uaig - nis!
gone my ___ vig - our Since thus I wan - der lone - ly!

Ó! slán is céad ón dtaobh so uaim
Cois Máighe na gcaor, na gcraobh, na gcruach,
Na stáid, na séad, na saor, na slua,
Na ndán, na ndréacht, na dtréan gan ghruaim!

Is och, ochón! is breóite mise,
Gan chuid, gan chóir, gan chóip, gan chisde,
Gan sult, gan seód, gan spórt, gan spionna,
O seóladh me chun uaignis!

Slán tar aon don té dar dual,
An bháinchnis bhéasach, bhéaltais, bhuadhach,
Chuir tráth chun sléi me i gcéin am ruaig,
'Sí grá mo chléibh, bé 'n-Éirinn cuach!

Is fánach faon mé, is fraochmhar fuar,
Is támh-lag tréith, 's is taomach trua,
I mbarr an tsléi gan aon, mo nuar!
Am páirt ach fraoch is gaoth adtuaidh!

Ó dháil an chléir dham céile nua,
Cois Máighe go h-éag ní h-é mo chuairt,
Go bráth lem ré táim réidh lem chuaich,
Le mnáibh an tsaol chuir me ar buairt.

Is och, ochón! mo bhrón, mo mhille!
Iomarca an óil is póga bruinneall
Chuir mise lem laethibh gan fód, gan fuithin,
Fós gan iomad fuadair!

AINDRIAS MAG CRAITH

A long farewell I send to thee,
Fair Maigue of corn and fruit and tree,
Of state and gift and gathering grand,
Of song, romance and chieftain bland!

And och, ochón! dark fortune's rigour,
Wealth, title, tribe of glorious figure,
Feast, gift—all gone, and gone my vigour
Since thus I wander lonely!

Farewell to her to whom 'tis due,
The fair-skinned, gentle, mild-lipped, true,
For whom exiled o'er the hills I go,
My heart's dear love, whate'er my woe!

Cold, homeless, worn, forsaken, lone,
Sick, languid, faint, all comfort flown,
On the wild hill's height I'm hopeless cast,
To wail to the heath and the northern blast!

Forced by the priest my love to flee,
Fair Maigue through life I ne'er shall see,
And must my beauteous bird forgo,
And all the sex that wrought me woe!

And och, ochón! my grief, my ruin!
'Twas drinking deep and beauty wooing
That caused through life my whole undoing
And left me wandering lonely!

EDWARD WALSH

93

1. I send farewell and a hundred from this place To the Maigue of the berries, the branches, the corn-stacks, Of the stately women, the jewels, the freemen, the hosts, Of the poems, the songs, the joyous heroes.

Chorus. Alas, alas! 'tis sickly I am, Without possessions or rights, without company or treasure, Without pleasure or property, without sport or vigour, Since I was driven to solitude.

2. Farewell above all to her to whom 'tis due, The mannerly, white-skinned girl, soft-lipped and gifted, Who has caused my exile for a space to the far hills, She is the love of my breast, whoe'er the maid be!

3. Wandering and weak am I, frantic and cold, Fainting and lonely, moody and sad, On the mountain-top with no one, alas! To share my solitude except heather and the north wind.

4. Since the clergy have decreed for me a new spouse, I shall never again visit Maigue-side till death, For the rest of my days I have bidden goodbye to my sweetheart, And to the women of the world who brought me to sorrow.

Last Chorus. Alas, alas! my grief and my ruin! Immoderate drinking and kissing girls Have left me for ever without hearth or home, And even with very little energy.

Aindrias Mag Craith (Andrew Magrath) was a licentious man but a gifted rhymer who spent most of his time as a hedge-school master in the little town of Croom, County Limerick. This pretty spot is on the banks of the river Maigue, about nine miles from Limerick City in the direction of Charleville. The district was a home of poets in the eighteenth century, chief among whom were Magrath and his friend Seán Ó Tuama (John O'Toomey), who kept the local inn.

His contemporaries rarely called Magrath by his proper appellation. Instead, they used the nickname of "*An Mangaire Súgach*" ("The Jolly Pedlar"), which he acquired early in his career as the result of a practical joke. Having fallen out with the local priest because of his manner of life, he offered himself to the parson as a convert to Protestantism, but was refused for the same reason: an imbroglio which he made the theme of a witty lament. The circumstances in which he wrote his "Farewell to the Maigue" are sufficiently explained by the song itself. Magrath died at an advanced age some time after 1790 and is said to be buried in Kilmallock.

This tune will be seen to resemble the preceding tune in some of its bars; but the general likeness is hardly close enough for the two airs to be regarded as variants.

A GHAOTH ANDEAS !　　　O SOUTH WIND!

Allegretto

"A ghaoth a - ndeas— na mbraon mbog glas, A ní— gach fai - the
"O south— wind of— the gen - tle rain, You ban - ish win - ter's

féar - mhar, Bheir iasg— ar eas— is grian i dteas, Is líon— is meas— ar
weath - er, Bring sal - mon to— the pool a - gain, The bees— a - mong— the

ghéag - aibh, Má's síos ar fad— mar mbínn féin seal Is
heath - er: If north - ward now— you mean to blow, As you

mian - ach leat - sa séid - e, Cuir - im Rí na bhFeart— dhod
rust - le soft— a - bove me, God - speed be with— you

chaomh - int ar neart, 'S túir don tír— sin blas— mo bhéil - se!"
as you go, With a kiss— for those— that love me!"

(*File*)
" A ghaoth andeas na mbraon mbog glas,
　A ní gach faithe féarmhar,
Bheir iasg ar eas is grian i dteas,
　Is líon is meas ar ghéagaibh,
Más síos ar fad mar mbínn féin seal
　Is mianach leat-sa séide,
Cuirim Rí na bhFeart dhod chaomhaint ar neart,
　'S túir don tír sin blas mo bhéil-se! "

(*Gaoth*)
" Sínim andeas a' díonamh cleas
　Nach ndíonann neach sa' saol so,
Mar íslím gaimh is sgaoilim leac
　Is díbrim sneacht' as sléibhte.
Ó taoi tú ar lear go bhfuí tú mo neart,
　'S gur mian liom do leas a dhéanamh,
Go bhfúigfe mé mo bheannacht ins gach aon tslí ar maith leat,
　Agus choíche i gCathair Éamoinn! "

(*File*)
" A Chonnachta an tsóidh, an tsuilt is an spóirt,
　I n-imirt 's i n-ól an fhíona,
Sin chugaibh mo phóg ar rith ins a' ród,
　Leigim le seól gaoithe í.
Tá mise beó i mboige na seód,
　Mar a mbrúitear gach sórt bídh dhom,
Ach is mian liom fós tarraing d'bhur gcomhair
　Muna gcluine mé ach ceól píopa! "

DOMHNALL MEIRGEACH MAC CON MARA

(*Poet*)
" O south wind of the gentle rain,
　You banish winter's weather,
Bring salmon to the pool again,
　The bees among the heather.
If northward now you mean to blow,
　As you rustle soft above me,
God-speed be with you as you go,
　With a kiss for those that love me! "

(*Wind*)
" From south I come with velvet breeze,
　My work all nature blesses,
I melt the snow and strew the leas
　With flowers and soft caresses.
I'll help you to dispel your woe,
　With joy I'll take your greeting
And bear it to your loved Mayo
　Upon my wings so fleeting! "

(*Poet*)
" My Connacht, famed for wine and play,
　So leal, so gay, so loving,
Here's a fond kiss I send to-day,
　Borne by the wind in its roving.
These Munster folk are good and kind,
　Right royally they treat me,
But this land I'd gladly leave behind,
　With your Connacht pipes to greet me! "

DONAL O'SULLIVAN

95

1. " O wind from the south with the soft clear drops, You that make every sward grassy, Bring the fish to the waterfall, give heat to the sun And abundance of fruit to the branches, If it is far to the north where I once lived That you are minded to blow, May the King of Power preserve you in strength, And give the taste of my mouth to that country ! "

2. " I blow from the south, performing feats Which no one else on earth can do, For I lay winter low and scatter the ice, And banish the snow from the mountains. Since you are in need(?) you shall have my strength, And I am fain to succour you, I shall leave my blessing in every place you choose, And always in Caher Edmund ! "

3. " O blissful, joyous, sporting Connacht, Home of gaming and of wine-drinking, Here goes my kiss to you rushing along the road, I send it on the wings of the wind. I am living in splendid luxury, Where every kind of food is dressed for me, But yet I am fain to draw towards you, If I should hear but the music of the pipes ! "

Nothing appears to be known of the author of this song, except that he was a native of Irrul, County Mayo, named Domhnall Meirgeach Mac Con Mara (Freckled Donal Macnamara). Caher Edmund, mentioned in the second verse, is a townland in the parish of Ballinrobe in that county.

SLÁN CHUN CARRAIG AN ÉIDE FAREWELL TO CARRAIG AN ÉIDE*

Poco pesante

Slán ag-us da-thad le ceang-al ceart dío-ghrais Chun gach
Fare-well and two score to loved bonds that en-twined me, To the

áit-reabh is bail' ó Chill Ait-chidh go Foinn-seann: An____
peop-le and plac-es I'm leav-ing be-hind me: From Kill-

báin-tsliocht 'n-a gcleacht-ainn-se beath-uis-ge brío-mhar,
-at-ty to Funch-eon's the spot that I speak of, Where we

Dán-ta le n-ai-thir-is is____ spreag-air-eacht chaoin-phort;
sport-ed and played, drink-ing____ more than I reck of;

Rinn-ce 'gus pléir-eacht ag béi-thibh gan____ tlás,
A bev-y of maids, full of charm and al____ lure, With

Sgaoith bhruinn-eall saor-dha____ lem thaobh-sa go sámh, Go____
sing-ing and danc-ing____ my sad-ness would cure, So____

-síod-ach, go séan-mhar, go séimh sult-mhar cáidh. Is____
gen-tle, so lov-ing, so kind and de-mure. De-

cann-tlach 's is ca-thach le seal-ad mé 'ndaoir-se, Go____
-ject-ed and wear-y in thral-dom I wan-der, With no

h-amh-grach a' tais-teal, gan ait-eas ná aoibh-neas.
joy in my heart, though it grows ev-er fond-er.

Slán agus dathad le ceangal ceart díoghrais
Chun gach áitreabh is baile ó Chill Aitchidh go
    Foinnseann:
An báin-tsliocht 'n-a gcleachtainn-se beath-uisge
    bríomhar,
Dánta le n-aithris is spreagaireacht chaoin-phort;
    Rinnce 'gus pléireacht ag béithibh gan tlás,
    Sgaoith bhruinneall saordha lem thaobh-sa go sámh,
    Go síodach, go séanmhar, go séimh sultmhar cáidh.
Is canntlach 's is cathach le sealad mé i ndaoirse,
Go h-amhgrach a' taisteal, gan aiteas ná aoibhneas.

*Pronounced Corrig an Aedy.

Farewell and two score to loved bonds that
    entwined me,
To the people and places I'm leaving behind me.
From Killatty to Funcheon's the spot that I speak of,
    Where we sported and played, drinking more
        than I reck of.
    A bevy of maids, full of charm and allure,
    With singing and dancing my sadness would cure,
    So gentle, so loving, so kind and demure:
Dejected and weary in thraldom I wander,
With no joy in my heart, though it grows ever fonder.

Mo shlán-sa tar éinne san tsaogal chun Liam ghil,
Fear grámhar deigh-mhéinneach glan-tréitheach
   caoin ciallmhar,
Ráib sultmhar saordha le féile do riaradh
Na táinte go féastach in' aol-bhrogh le mian suilt:
  Éigse na laoi-cheast, cléir, draoithe 'gus dáimh,
  Tréad thaistil tíortha gach n-oíche 'gus lá,
  Béithe 'gus saoithe, doill, naoidhin agus báird,
Go fíontach go feólmhar go beórach go biamhar,
Go líonmhar go lónnrach go ceólmhar go siansach.

Mo shlán-sa chun Seágain, fear grámhar neamh-chinnte,
'San tábhairne ba ghnáthach a' trádh *punch* im chuíreann;
Bába na mbán-bhrollach n-áille 'gus saoithe,
Sámh-chrota sáir-bhinne ghrádhfadh 'n-a thímcheall;
  Slán agus céad le searc saor chun Liam,
  Grá is gean mo chléibh is caoin-chéile le cian
  Do bhábaibh an léighinn-tsrotha shaobh-chamann ciall.
Mo shlán-sa chun Domhnaill, an t-óg-gas lán d'aoibhneas,
Is Tomás beag mo stór-sa, do phógainn le díoghras.

Slán cuirim páirteach gan áireamh ó chéile
Chun Ádaimh, chun Seágain, chun Máire 's chun Séamais;
Slán chun Neil mhánla, caoin-ghrá 's searc mo chléibh-se,
D'fhuil ársa Eochaidh ádhmhair, ceap dáimhe 'gus éigse.
  Mo shlán chun an Róistigh, fear ceólmhar, guth-bhinn,
  Le gáirdeas do thógadh gach ceó-bhruid dem chroí.
  Mo shlán chun gach óg-fhlaith ba mheón liom-sa 'ríomh
Le h-áthas fá thearman Charraig an Éide—
Óm fhán-rith dá gcasainn ní sgarfainn lem ré libh!

EOGHAN RUA Ó SÚILLEABHÁIN

Farewell, first and best, to friend William the hearty,
Warm-hearted, free-handed, the man for a party!
In his mansion he'd welcome his friends without
  number,
For converse, for drinking, for dining or slumber.
  The sage and the scholar, the poet, the priest,
  Blind, halt, young and old were all bid to the feast.
  At his table good victuals and wines never ceased
Till succeeded by music, by dancing and singing,
Sweet sounds whose faint echo e'en now is still ringing.

Farewell, too, to Johnny in fair or ill weather,
Farewell to the inn where we quaffed punch together,
Farewell to the white-bosomed girls and the sages
Who'd learnedly discourse from history's pages.
  Farewell with affection both heart-felt and strong
  To William, my loved one, who now for so long
  Is wed to the muses of music and song.
Farewell to young Donal, and—how I shall miss him!—
Baby Thomas, my darling, I'd kiss him and kiss him!

A tender farewell, with a love that won't vary,
To Adam, to John, and to James and to Mary.
Farewell to bright Nell, with my love and affection,
Her beauty I'll cherish in fond recollection.
  Farewell, too, to Roche of the merry blue eye,
  Whose singing would rival the lark in the sky.
  Farewell to them all, and a loving good-bye
To Carraig an Éide, best-loved and true-hearted,
If I ever return we shall never be parted!

DONAL O'SULLIVAN

1. Farewell and forty, with a true bond of affection, To every dwelling and homestead from Killatty to Funcheon: To the boon companions amongst whom I was wont to enjoy good whiskey, With poems being recited and soft music a-playing; Dancing with maidens and dalliance without surcease, A bevy of charming girls tranquilly beside me—Elegant they were and happy, beautiful, merry and virtuous. Sorrowful and dejected am I for a space, in servitude, Distressfully journeying without joy or pleasure.

2. My farewell above all in this world to dear William, That lovable and sincere man, accomplished, gentle and wise: A generous happy fellow who would hospitably entertain Multitudes at a feast in his white mansion, with a mind for jollity; Poets learned in matters literary, clergy, wiseacres, men of letters, The crowd of those who roam the country night and day, Girls and sages, blind people, children and bards, With lavish wine and meat, beer and victuals, Amid scenes of plenty and brightness and music and bliss.

3. My farewell to John, the amiable and open-handed, Who was accustomed in the tavern to drain punch in my company; He would love fair, white-bosomed maidens and clever men With soothing, tuneful harp-music around him. Farewell and a hundred with deep affection to William, The love and fondness of my breast and a gentle spouse for long Of the maidens of learning's stream who bemuse the brain [i.e., the muses who inspire poetic frenzy]. My farewell to Donal, the young lad full of merriment, And little Thomas, my darling whom I used to kiss so devotedly.

4. I send an equal farewell, without singling one from another, To Adam, to John, to Mary and to James. Farewell to gentle Nell, the dear love of my breast, Of the race of fortunate Eochaidh, the ancestor of poets and rhymers. My farewell to Roche, the musical and sweet-voiced, Whose drollery would lift all melancholy from my heart. My farewell to every young hero I would wish to mention With happiness within the confines of Carraig an Éide. If I return from my wandering I shall not part from you for the rest of my days!

This touching farewell was written by Eoghan Rua Ó Súilleabháin (Owen O'Sullivan, called "*Rua*" from his red hair), who in lyrical genius, command of language and sheer beauty of expression excels all the other Irish poets of the eighteenth century. He was born in 1748, about seven miles east of Killarney, County Kerry, and we know little of his early years; but from his mastery of word-weaving in his native tongue—a mastery never achieved before or since—it is obvious that he received a sound education in one of the hedge-schools—the only establishments which the Penal Laws allowed to Catholics of humble birth in his time. He also knew English, in which he composed a few poems of indifferent merit; and a reference in one of them suggests that he was familiar with Pope and Dryden.

Schoolmaster, farm labourer, soldier and sailor by turns, Owen Rua led a restless and (it must be confessed) a somewhat disordered life: a fact that need neither surprise nor shock us when we remember that in the Munster of his day all prospects of a career suited to the intellectual attainments of such a man were denied to him on the ground of his religion. He appears to have joined the British Army in 1774 or thereabouts, sojourning in England, but returned home a few years later; and it is certain that he was present (either as a sailor or in the marines) at Rodney's great naval victory off Guadeloupe, in the West Indies, over the French Admiral de Grasse, 12th April, 1782. Returned from the wars, he met his death in June, 1784, at the age of thirty-six, as the result of a blow on the head in a tavern brawl at Killarney. Though his burial place is a matter of uncertainty, it is probable that he lies hard by in the Abbey of Muckross.

Owen Rua spent part of his time as a hired labourer on the rich riparian lands of the noble river Blackwater, in County Cork, and another of his songs, "The Mower", included in the present volume (p. 134), was composed in this locality. Carraig an Éide is a picturesque riverside spot about a mile and a half above Fermoy, which at that time consisted merely of a cluster of cabins and one tavern, where poor Owen had an amorous adventure frankly recounted in one of his poems. The Hydes, a family of English origin, built a mansion at Carraig an Éide in the late eighteenth century and changed its name to Castlehyde in accordance with the bad practice of the period.

The beauty of the present piece lies partly in its sustained musical rhythm (quite untranslatable in English) and partly in the deep sincerity which permeates it. From the internal evidence of one of the verses (here omitted), it would appear to have been written on the eve of the poet's departure overseas—probably about 1774, when he joined the army. Owen seems determined to remember with affection everyone, young and old, who was kind to him or whose company gave him pleasure: not merely those dwelling in Carraig an Éide, such as his host, William Barry and his wife Mary, the poet's namesake, but all the neighbours, from Killatty three miles to the west to where the river Funcheon joins the Blackwater just east of Fermoy. Incidentally, the whole poem gives a charming picture of the social life of the well-to-do Munster farmers of the period.

The personage mentioned in the last verse is *Eochaidh Aontsúla* ("Eochaidh the One-eyed"), ancestor of the O'Sullivans, who is supposed to have lived in the sixth century. It is said that a druid from Scotland, hearing that Eochaidh could never refuse a request, asked him for one of his eyes—which the owner forthwith plucked out and gave to him. The story is told as typifying the traditional generosity of the O'Sullivans—a subject on which I do not feel competent to express an opinion.

RELIGIOUS SONGS

Unlike most countries, Ireland has no vernacular hymnology, and the reason is neither religious nor literary, but historical. The purpose of hymns is to assist the devotion of the faithful at church services, and their singing by the congregation is a corporate act of worship. The period within which such a hymnology might have been expected to arise and to establish itself was from about 1700 onwards, when Irish was the general language of the nation. But this was precisely the period when the Penal Laws were in force, and over a great part of the country corporate acts of worship were hardly possible. The faithful could hear Mass only by stealth, in circumstances of some danger to both priest and people. Moreover, in the chaotic conditions that prevailed from the educational and cultural standpoint the printing of books in Irish was out of the question; and in any case the vast majority of the people were unable to read their native tongue.

However, the religion of the Irish is no Sunday religion but one in which the eternal truths are never far from the forefront of consciousness and so, though they wrote no hymns, they created a large mass of religious verse, to be sung or recited while at work in the home or in the fields or used as part of their morning and evening devotions. This verse is of two types. The first is the purely folk product which, though often lacking the elaborate artistry of Irish literary verse, is informed by an intensely devotional spirit. Many of these pieces are probably of considerable antiquity and perhaps owe their preservation from remote times to the promise added on at the end that the reciters will receive some miraculous or heavenly blessing. "The Lament of the Blessed Virgin" is an example of this first type.

The second consists of sacred songs by known authors. However humble their calling in the late eighteenth and early nineteenth centuries—Hoare, for instance, was a blacksmith and Denn a chapel clerk—such men were the heirs of a proud tradition of scholarship, stretching right back (so far as religious verse is concerned) through the intermediate stage of a Seán na Ráithíneach or an Ó Bruadair to the bardic poetry of Donnchadh Mór Ó Dálaigh in the thirteenth century. Their songs were written to the folk airs current in their time. Curiously enough, they often chose melodies associated in the popular mind with words which (to say the least) were extremely secular in character: possibly because, like Rowland Hill, they "did not see any reason why the devil should have all the good tunes."

Looking at this body of religious verse as a whole, can we predicate anything of the spirit which gave rise to it? Generalizations are dangerous, but it would seem that the Irish mind showed an undue preoccupation with the frailty of human nature, the hideousness of sin and the horror of eternal damnation: aspects which are certainly part of the picture but which, unless viewed in conjunction with the abounding love of God for His creatures, are joyless and pallid. One feels that these poets, known or unknown, would have understood and shared to the full Milton's anxiety to live his life "as ever in my great Task-Master's eye".

This would have been the appropriate section in which to include a specimen of carols, if such existed. But the tradition of carol-singing never seems to have taken root in Gaelic Ireland and, so far as I am aware, there are no carols in the Irish language.

AITHRÍ SHEÁIN DE HÓRA   THE REPENTANCE OF JOHN HOARE

A Mhic Mhuire na ngrás do cuireadh chun báis
    Is d'fhuiling an pháis pheannaideach,
Do cheannuigh síol Ádhaimh le h-allus do chnámh,
    Fola 'gus cneá dearga:
Freagair me, a ghrá, beir m'anam i dtráth
    Go Parrathas lán-ghradamach,
A' caitheamh a' tsóláis fhada ghil bhreá
    'Dir apstail is árd-aingealaibh.

Freagair me, a Chríost, a chara mo chroí,
    An charraig seo im chlí corruigh í,
'S óm dhearca leig síos sruthaibh aithrí
    Do bhéarfas go crích fhlathais me.
Mar is peacach me bhí sgannalach síor,
    Droich-bheartach, fíor-mhalluithe:
Ná hagair-se baois bheartaibh an tsaoil
    Ar mh'anam le linn sgartha liom.

Ní lia le rá gaineamh na trá,
    Ná drúcht ar bharr glasara,
Ná pcaca lc suíomh ar m'anam, fóiríor!
    Ceangailte am chroí calcaithe:
Cé mór a dtrian róm san tsliabh,
    Ní fhoghnann ciach eagla,
'S gur mó le léamh grása Dé
    Ná a ndearnaidh an saol d'ainfhios.

Son of Mary Who died between thieves crucified
    As the lance pierced Thy side on the Tree,
Redeeming our race by the sweat of Thy face
    And Thy blood poured apace o'er the lea:
Dear God, hear my cry! take my soul when I die
    To join Thee on high with Thy blest,
For ever and aye to share in their joy,
    And with rapture to lie on Thy breast.

Sweet Jesus Who art in heaven apart,
    Soften this heart like a stone!
And cause from mine eyes contrite tears to arise,
    So the heavenly prize may be won!
For I'm sunken in sin since my life did begin,
    Not recking the pain given Thee,
But at my life's end Thy grace to me lend,
    Be Thou still my friend! Succour me!

As many as be the sands of the sea,
    Or the dewdrops at even so bright,
Not less is the scroll of the sins on my soul,
    Blacker than coal in Thy sight.
For the dread Day of Doom when Thy judgement shall come
    This heart fills with gloom while I live,
Yet a penitent's sighs Thou wilt not despise,
    Thou wilt bid me arise—and forgive!

Féach mar do shéan Peadar Mac Dé
  An tan lagaigh an tréad malluithe é,
'S nuair d'aistrigh sé i gcreathaibh aithmhéil'
  Gur glacadh san réim bheannuithe é.
Dob fheasach don tsaol fhairsing go léir
  Gur pheacach bhí ar strae Magdalen,
'S dá chuirpeacht é a beatha le léamh
  Go dtug sile na mbraon flaitheas di.

Sgreadaim is éim, aitchim go séimh,
  Ar Mhuire 's a h-Aon-Mhac calama,
Teacht sealad fá dhéin m'anma a' plé,
  Dá chosaint ón maor malluithe:
Deisgiobuil Dé 's a charaid go léir
  Am tharraing san réim bheannuithe,
Mo bhearta ar an saol cealgach claon
  Ganguideach baoth a mhaitheamh dam.

SEÁN DE HÓRA

See how Peter denied his Shepherd and Guide
  When the Jews him espied in the hall,
But his grief unsuppressed was rewarded at last
  With a place midst the blest over all.
And Mary Magdalèn was known among men
  For the depth of her sin and her shame,
Yet her tears so contrite washed her soul snowy white,
  And a saint in Thy sight she became.

Our Lady so mild, by sin undefiled,
  Plead with thy Child at my death
From heaven to descend my soul to defend
  Against the arch-fiend and his scaith.
For 'tis Jesus alone my ill-deeds can atone,
  My follies, my proneness to sin,
All fears to dispel from the demons of hell
  And to Paradise welcome me in!

DONAL O'SULLIVAN

1. O Son of gracious Mary Who wast put to death And suffered the torment of the Passion, Who redeemed Adam's seed with the sweat of Thy bones, [With] bleedings and gory wounds: Hear me, Beloved, bring my soul in due time To the abounding glory of Paradise, In the enjoyment of eternal bliss, bright and splendid, Between the apostles and the archangels.

2. Hear me, O Christ, Friend of my heart, Move this rock that is in my breast, And from mine eyes cause to flow a flood of contrite tears That will bear me to the land of heaven. For I am a sinner that ever was shameful, A man of evil deeds, truly wicked: And do not visit my life's acts of folly On my soul when it is parting from me (i.e. from my body).

3. Not more numerous to mention are the sands of the seashore, Or the dewdrops on top of the verdure, Than the sins that may be proved against my soul, alas! Bound to my stagnate heart. Though [even] one third of them would be a large number to confront me at the Day of Judgement, Torment of fear is uncalled for, Since the grace of God is greater in the telling Than all the unrighteousness of the world.

4. Behold how Peter denied the Son of God On the occasion when the accursed flock laid hold of Him, And when he turned to trembling penance How he was received among the blest. It was well known to the entire wide world That Magdalen was an erring sinner, But however vicious the story of her life Weeping tears [of contrition] brought her to heaven.

5. I cry and implore, I gently beseech, Mary and her dauntless Only Son To come pleading for a space to succour my soul, To defend it from the prince of evil: May God's disciples and all those that love Him Draw me in among the blest, Forgiving me the deeds of my wayward and wicked life, With its deceit and its folly.

This song, instinct with religious feeling, was written by a Munster poet of the eighteenth century named Seán De Hóra (John Hoare). He was a native of County Cork and migrated as a young man to Doonaha, south of Kilkee, County Clare, where he practised his trade as a blacksmith until his death about 1780.

Gile mo chroí do chroí-se,____ 'Shlán - a-thóir! Is
Light of my__ heart Thy Heart, O_____ Lord_____ div - ine!

cis-te__ mo__chroí do chroí-se d'fháil im chóir! Ós_ foll - us__ gur
Pulse of__ my__heart Thy Heart to have for mine! And_ since for__love of

líon do____ chroí_____ dhom ghrá - sa, 'stór, I
me Thy___ Sac - red Heart_____ did fill, With -

gcoch - all mo chroí__ do chroí - se fág i gcomhad!
- in_____ my heart___ fast - bound_____ Thy Heart be still!

Gile mo chroí do chroí-se, a Shlánathóir!
Is ciste mo chroí do chroí-se d'fháil im chóir!
Ós follus gur líon do chroí dhom ghrá-sa, a stór,
I gcochall mo chroí do chroí-se fág i gcomhad!

Ar fhuilingis trínn-ne, a Rí ghil árd na gcomhacht,
Ní thigeann im smaointe a shuidheamh ná a
    thrácht i gcóir:
'S gur le goraghoin nimhe do chroí 's do chneá-sa,
    a stór,
Do bhrostuigh na mílte saoi go sámh i gcoróinn.

A Athair 's a Íosa, dhíon let bhás me beó,
'S do dhealbh mo ghnaoi gan chríochna ceárd it chló,
Nach danardha an gníomh, a Chríost, nár
    ghrádhas-sa fós
Ach gach uile ní 'n-a mbíodh do ghráin don tsórt!

Ar shealabhaigh Maois det dhlí-se i bpáirt an tslóigh
Do b'annamh mo chroí-se síoch ná sásta leó:
Ach fala 'gus fraoch-nimh, craos is cárna stóir,
Le h-easmailt gach n-aon is na mílte cáin ba mhó!

Le h-atuirse chnaoite suidheamh a ndeárna geóbhad,
'Taisteal gach tíre i gcríochaibh Fháilbhe is Eoghain,
Ag aithris mo ghníomhra 's a' caoi le gártha
    bróin,
Is a' sgreada go sgíosmhar tríd, a' tál na ndeór.

Nuair chasfad-sa arís let ghuí-se, a bhláth na n-Órd,
Fé thearmann Chríost is díon a ghrásta am chomhad,
Beidh garbh-chnuic fhraoigh na líog
    do chrádhadh mé róm,
'N-a machairí míne síoda 's 'n-a mbánta sróill.

Light of my heart Thy Heart, O Lord divine!
Pulse of my heart Thy Heart to have for mine!
And since for love of me Thy Sacred Heart did fill,
Within my heart fast-bound Thy Heart be still!

Thy travail for us, dear Lord, is all unguessed,
Thine anguish, Thy pain, abide within Thy
    breast:
But yet Thy bleeding Heart our human want
    supplies,
And speeds unnumbered blest to Paradise.

O Son of God, Who dying didst me save
And in Thy likeness didst my features grave,
Shameful the deed, O Christ, that thus far I have
    loved
Naught but whate'er from Thee is far removed!

Thy laws received by Moses on the Mount,
These did I break more oft than I can count:
Lusting instead for gluttony, wrath and pride,
Avarice, envy, sloth and all beside!

In bitter grief I'll range both far and near,
Telling my tale of sin for all to hear,
Wailing each trespass dire with sad and
    contrite cries,
Waking the hills with tearful agonies.

Through Mary's prayer I'll turn to mine own place,
Welcomed by Christ and shielded by His grace:
The rough and stony hills that troubled my lost
    youth
Are now as level plains and satin-smooth.

Ar fán cé bhís-se, a Rí ghil naomhtha, ó neamh,
Go cráite trínn-ne i slí nach léir a mheas,
Do ghrá-sa, a Chríost, níor mhaoidhis gur réab
    an tsleagh
Árus dín it chroí don tsaol ar fad!
        TADHG GAEDHLACH Ó SÚILLEABHÁIN

O King of Kings, e'en though Thou didst descend
From heaven's portals our poor lives to mend,
'Twas through the cruel lance Thy burning love
    designed
A bourn within Thy Heart for all mankind!
        DONAL O'SULLIVAN

1. Thy Heart is the light of my heart, O Saviour! To possess Thy Heart for mine own is my heart's treasure. Since it is manifest that Thy Heart did fill with love for me, Beloved, Leave Thy Heart in keeping in the recesses of my heart!

2. What Thou didst suffer for us, O bright high King of powers, My thoughts are unable adequately to state or to describe: But it was through the fierce warming laceration of Thy Heart and Thy wounds, Beloved, That unnumbered blest sped gently to the crown.

3. Father and Jesus, Who by Thy death didst secure my life, And Who without exhausting Thine artistry didst fashion my countenance after Thy likeness, Is it not a sorry deed, O Christ, that thus far I have loved Only all those things which Thou dost abhor!

4. The laws which Moses received on behalf of the multitude, Seldom was my heart reconciled to them or satisfied, But with envy and envenomed rage, gluttony and covetousness, With reviling of everybody and grievous faults by the thousand.

5. With bitter sorrow I shall make a tale of my trespasses, Faring throughout every region within the confines of Fáilbhe and Eoghan [Ireland], Recounting my deeds and lamenting with cries of contrition, Shrieking wearily through it all, weeping copious tears.

6. When I return again by thy prayer, O flower of the Orders [the Blessed Virgin], Under the shield of Christ, with the protection of His grace preserving me, The rough, stone-covered, heathery hills that were wont to torment me will be As smooth, silken plains and pastures of satin.

7. A wanderer from heaven though Thou wert, O bright, holy King, Agonized through us in a manner that may not be measured, Thy love, O Christ, Thou didst not make manifest until the lance broke open A protecting abode in Thy Heart for all mankind!

Tadhg Gaedhlach Ó Súilleabháin is the chief of the modern Irish religious poets. (The epithet *Gaedhlach*, meaning "Irish", probably implies that he had a rustic appearance.) He was born about 1715, almost certainly in County Limerick, but spent most of his life in the neighbouring counties of Cork and Waterford. In the earlier part of his career his output was similar to that of other poets of the period—patriotic pieces, elegies, verse-letters to his friends and so forth. But in late middle life he experienced a change of heart and thereafter, with few exceptions, he wrote none but religious poetry, much of it of a very high order, spending his days in penance, prayer and works of sanctity. He died on the 22nd April, 1795 while engaged in his devotions in the *Séipéal Mór* or Cathedral of Waterford City, and he is buried in the churchyard of Ballylaneen, near Kilmacthomas. His friend and fellow-poet Donncha Rua Mac Con Mara (for whom see the notes to the song "*Bán-Chnuic Éireann Ó*" at p. 91 in this collection) wrote his epitaph in polished Latin elegiacs, and this is now inscribed on his tombstone.

The hypermetrical third line in each verse of my translation, while not absolutely essential for musical purposes, avoids the awkwardness of singing an undue number of notes to one syllable.

Tadhg Gaedhlach's sacred poems attained great popularity in his lifetime, though they circulated only in manuscript. In 1802 they were printed in Clonmel with the title *Timothy O'Sullivan's Irish Pious Miscellany*, a book which in the first half of the nineteenth century enjoyed a wider circulation than any other written in the Irish language. It ran into several editions, the later ones being edited by Patrick Denn, who is the author of the song which follows.

Ar mo leaba dham aréir is mé a' déanamh marana
Ar aindeise an tsaoghail is méid a mhallathacht,
   Ochón! 's is olc é mar ghnó!
A' brise 's a' réaba dlí an Aen-Mhic bheannuithe,
'S gan suim 'n-a bhréithre ná géill dá aitheanta,
   Ochón! is danaid é dhóibh!
'Sea thuigeas-sa an t-éacht tá ar strae 's ar mearathal,
Ceangailte ar shéirse age daol dá mealla so
Go h-ifreann craosach fá shéala a ndamanta,
I dtaobh Críost do shéana tré claon a n-anama,
   Ochón! faoi mhallacht go deó!

As sleepless yestreen I lay and pondered
On all who from Christ's strait path have wandered,
   Ochone! how grievous my tale!
Neglecting His laws, His words, His preaching,
Paying small heed to His life and teaching,
   Ochone! 'tis theirs to bewail!
I thought of the numbers that, virtue hating,
Are eager prey to the wiles of Satan,
With manifold sin their appetites sating,
I thought of the doom that is them awaiting,
   Ochone! all burning in hell!

'S an chuid don dtrúp san thug cúl don mbeannathacht,
Dream na drúise chuireann dúil sa' mbarbaracht,
 Ochón! is fuath liom a sórt!
Is lucht na mionn mór atá go duairc ceangailte
Ag diabhail is deamhain le slabhra an pheaca san,
 Ochón! is pianfar iad fós!
Is lucht an éirligh léantach mhaslathach,
Tharcuisneach bhréagach sgéaltach sgannalach,
Is feallairí fraochmhar mar ghéirnimh chealagach,
Thugann aithis don Aon-Mhac go daor do cheannuigh sinn,
 Ochón! beid á losga go deó!

Atá dream eile fós ar sgórnain greamaithe,
Lucht meisge 'gus póite go deó bheidh damanta,
 Ochón! do dheasca a gcuid óil!
Mar tá an t-anam bocht múchta 'chúrsa mallathacht,
'S gan beann aca ar Dhia ná ar bhia na n-aingealaibh,
 Ochón! is fuathmhar é a nglór!
Le barbaracht, bréaga, le sgréacha, glamaireacht,
A' spalpa go h-éachtach, le faobhar-nimh ghangaideach,
Ó! is le bladhman, spreallaireacht mhillteach mhaslathach,
A' méadú an pheaca san do thuillfeadh damaint dóibh,
 Ochón! in ifreann go deó!

Chím gach caille-bhean liath agus iarmhar sheanduine
Go daingean mírialta 's gan iarra ar a leas aca,
 Ochón! nach dona é mar sgeól!
Ach go feargach faobhrach 's a mbéal go h-easgaineach,
A' tiomuint go h-éachtach créachta an Leanaibh sin,
 Ochón! peannaid go leór!
Dá losga ameasc daol fá phéin-bhroid damanta
Beidh óg agus aosta do thréig gach beannuitheacht,
Mara nglanfaid go h-éag a bpéarla ón bpaca dubh
Tré pháis Mhic Dé is le déaraibh aithreachais,
 Ochón! sin crích ar mo sgeól!

PÁDRAIG DENN

The part of the flock that is unregenerate,
Given to lust and to ways degenerate,
 Ochone! how hateful their sin!
Perjurers too, and those steeped in profanity,
Liars and thieves, the shame of humanity,
 Ochone! to demons akin!
Mongers of scandal of every variety,
Sinners who wallow in gross impropriety,
Spurning their crucified God with impiety,
Spawn of the devil indulged to satiety,
 Ochone! he'll welcome them in!

There's another class yet—the slaves of their gullet,
Who'd squander on drink the last groat in their wallet,
 Ochone! how swinish their ways!
For the food of the angels it's little they're caring,
Sodden with liquor, they're cursing and swearing,
 Ochone! instead of God's praise!
In place of repentance, almsgiving and fasting,
With gestures obscene and with language disgusting
They magnify sin with contemptible boasting,
Making full sure that in hell they'll be roasting,
 Ochone! they'll all be ablaze!

I see every crone and old man in the nation
Rebellious of soul and not seeking salvation,
 Ochone! all sunk in the mire!
Giving free rein to each vice ill beseemed them,
Turning their backs on the Christ Who redeemed them,
 Ochone! with scourging so dire!
Be sure young and old who God's graces are spurning
Eternally banished in hell will be burning,
Unless they repent and, from evil ways turning,
By cleansing their souls will be Paradise earning,
 Ochone! yet so as by fire!

DONAL O'SULLIVAN

1. On my bed last night as I was reflecting On the misery of the world and the extent of its wickedness, Alas! 'tis a sorry business! Breaking and violating the law of the blessed Only Son, Giving no heed to His words or obedience to His commandments, Alas! 'tis a pity for them! I realized the number that are straying and in error, Bound securely by the devil that is enticing them To gaping hell under the seal of their damnation, Because of denying Christ through the perversity of their souls, Alas! accursed for ever!

2. And the portion of that flock that turned their back on blessedness, The lustful class that have an appetite for obscenity, Alas! I loathe their kind! And those given to cursing who are direly bound To devils and demons through the fetters of that sin, Alas! they will be punished yet! And those given to injury who are grievous, insulting, Abusive, false, tale-bearing, scandal-loving, And furious deceivers like bitter, insidious poison, Who give shame to the Only Son Who redeemed us dearly, Alas! they will be burning for ever!

3. There is yet another class, gripped by the throat, The drunkards and tipplers who will be damned for eternity, Alas! because of their drink! For their wretched souls are smothered by reason of their wickedness, Caring nothing for God or for the food of the angels, Alas! their voices are detestable! With obscenity, lies, howling and screeching, Swearing terribly with bitter, envenomed spite, O! and with boasting and hurtful, offensive vulgarity, Increasing that sin that will earn damnation for them, Alas! in hell for ever!

4. I see every grey old hag and remnant of an old man Stubbornly undisciplined and not seeking their salvation, Alas! is it not a pitiful tale? But angry and passionate, with their lips cursing, Swearing fiercely by the wounds of that Child, Alas! torment a-plenty! Burned amidst devils beneath the painful captivity of damnation Young and old will be who forsook every blessing, Unless they cleanse till death their pearl from the black pack, Through the passion of the Son of God and with tears of contrition, Alas! that's the end of my tale!

Pádraig (Patrick) Denn was born about 1756 near Cappoquin, County Waterford, the son of a hedge-school master. A deeply religious man, he lived an uneventful life at Cappoquin, combining the duties of school-teacher and clerk of the chapel till his death on the 5th July, 1828. About 1819 he brought out a new edition of the *Pious Miscellany* (for which see the notes to the previous song), adding an Appendix containing religious poems by himself. Denn was as great a zealot as Tadhg Gaedhlach, but he was not in the scholarly tradition; and perhaps for that reason his more homely verses made a greater appeal to the people. However that may be, they achieved an immense popularity in Munster during the pre-Famine period, when Irish was the habitual language of the home; and Denn's edition of the *Pious Miscellany* was many times reprinted.

Andante

Caoin - e na Maighd - in - e 'ndiaidh a — h-Aen - Mhic.
The Vir - gin's la - ment for her Son and our Sav - iour.

Och och - ón ag - us och - ón Ó! Na trí ri - the's iad a
Och och - ón ag - us och - ón Ó! *If the three kings came 'tis*

theacht le n-a chéil - e: Och och - ón ag - us och - ón Ó!
sure they'd be say - ing: Och och - ón ag - us och - ón Ó!

Caoine na Maighdine i ndiaidh a h-Aen-Mhic.
    Och ochón! agus ochón Ó!
Na trí rithe 's iad a theacht le n-a chéile:
    Och ochón! agus ochón Ó!

" Dá bhfeicfimís arís é do gheóimís ár leath-sgéal leis,
Go bhfuímís maithúnachas uaidh 'n-ár gclaonta,

Fé mar fuair Máire Magdiléna,
Agus an bhean do chimil dó an t-éadach,

Nó an bhean thug trí bliana i bhfiabhras aerach,
Go bhfuair sí an tsláinte 's na grásda i n-aeneacht,

Nó an dall do sháidh an tsleagh tré n-a thaobh dheas,
Go bhfeaca sé a chuid fola 'n-a srothaibh tréana,

Agus dúirt gurbh' fhiú na céadta gach aon bhraon di,
Nó an gadaí dubh do bhí ar a láimh dheas."

" Caithfidh mo Leanbh-sa triall an gharrdha amáireach,
Agus Leabhar na Páise a thúirt 'n-a láimh leis."

" Glaéidh chúm na h-Aspail go léfead an Pháis dóibh."
" A Thiarna," arsa Peadar, " ní sgarfad-sa go bráth leat."
" Is fíor go séanfaidh do bhéal me trí h-uaire roim an lá amáireach."

Tháinig Iúdás dorcha, thug sé póg dó 's chroith sé lámh leis:
" A Iúdáis mhallaithe, ní beag duit me dhíol is gan me thúirt ar láimh dóibh."

Do cheangluíodar suas le córdaí crua cnáibe é,
Thugadar leó go dtí Pilate a thug spás dó.

" Cad é bhur gcúis ar an bhfear mór breá so,
Go bhfuil agaibh 'n-a thímpall a leithéid seo 'ghárda? "

" Deir sé gurab é ceann rí na nGiúdach é 's go bhfuil aige na grásda."
" Más é sin bhur gcúis air, sgagaim-se mo lámha as."

D'árduíodar leó go dtí Hérod gan spás é.
" Cad é bhur gcúis ar an bhfear mór breá so,
Go bhfuil agaibh 'n-a thímpall a leithéid seo 'ghárda? "

" Deir sé gurab é Mac Dé é 's go bhfuil aige na grásda."
" Do réir mar mheasaim-se is maith an chúis bháis í.

" Ceangluídh den phola é go dtí an dá uair dhéag amáireach,
Cuiridh púicín ar a shúilibh agus culaith an amadáin air.

" Ceangluídh suas le córdaí crua cnáibe é,
Caithidh bhur seile air is déinidh fé gáire.

" Bíodh buille ó gach duine air—an t-Aon-Mhac Mháire,
Téighidh sa' gharrdha is bainidh an crann is mó a' fás ann.

" Cuiridh ar an gCrois é a' fulang na daor-Pháise,
Cuiridh na tairngí géara gan truaimhéil dó tré n-a dheárnaibh."

D'árduíodar suas ar a nguailne go h-árd é,
'S do chaitheadar amach ar chlocha crua na sráide é.

" Is mithid dom ", ars an Mhaighdean, " dul a' fiosrú mo ghrá geal."
Do bhí a ceann sgaoilte is a cosa gan náda,
Is í a' bailiú a chuid fola os cionn an fhásaigh.

Do léim sí isteach is amach thar ghárda.
" Dia dhuit, a Mhic, nó an aithnid duit do mháthair? "
" Bíodh agat an fhoidhne agus gheó tú na grásda."

" A Leinbh, is mór é t'ualach is léig cuid de ar do Mháthair."
" Do gheallas féin é dh'iompar ar shon sliocht Áidim.
Iompruíodh gach éinne a chrosa, a Mháithrín."

Nuair a chualaidh na Giúdaigh na focail sin dá rá aca,
Thógadar suas ar a nguailne go h-árd í,
'S do chaitheadar amach ar chlocha crua na sráide í.

" Is fíor, más é Mac Dé é, go dtógfaidh sé a Mháthair."
Annsan do thóg sé suas le beartaibh anáirde í.

Thógadar suas go Crann na Páise é,
Agus chaitheadar anuas 'n-a chuailín cnámh é.
" Sin é agaibh anois é agus goilidh bhur sáth air."

" Ó! is fíor ", arsa Naomh Bríde, " ná fuil anois ach an sgáth ann.
Cá bhfuil na trí Mhuire go gcaoinfidís mo ghrá geal? "
Tháinig na trí aingil is do ghoileadar go cráite air.

Do ghoileadar ar dtúis thar cionn a n-Athar 's a Mháthar,
An dara h-uair thar cionn sliocht Áidim,
Agus an tríú h-uair thar cionn an pheacaigh ná filleann go bráth air.

" Sin é caoine na Maighdine; ach é bheith go ró-chráite,
Níl éinne agaibh-se go mbeidh aige an dán so,

Agus éinne adéarfaidh é, is a rá gach lá leis,
Ní fheicfidh mo Mhac-sa breith dhamanta go bráth air."

The Virgin's lament for her Son and our Saviour.
        Och ochón! agus ochón O!
If the three kings came, 'tis sure they'd be saying:
        Och ochón! agus ochón O!

" If we see Him again we shall ask for His blessing,
Obtaining forgiveness for all our transgressions,

As Magdalen did with sorrow unfailing,
And the woman who wiped His face with her veiling,

Or the woman who suffered three years from a fever,
Who found health and grace and a respite from grieving,

111

Or the soldier who pierced His side in his blindness,
And said, as the red blood was spouting beside him,

' Every drop of this blood will bring profit to millions,'
Or the penitent thief who was promised the Kingdom."

" In the Garden to-morrow my Child will be passing,
Holding in hand the Book of His Passion."

" Call Me the Apostles, My Passion to recite them."
" Master," said Peter, " I'll always stay by Thee."
" Before cock-crow to-morrow three times thou'lt deny Me."

Dark Judas came, with a kiss he waylaid Him:
" Judas accursèd! dost seek to betray Me?"

With hard ropes of hemp securely they bound Him,
And brought Him to Pilate, all surging around Him.

" This fine tall man—with what do you charge Him,
Finding it meet so straitly to guard Him?"

" His claim is that He is the King of all Jewry."
" I wash my hands—let yourselves see to it."

From Pilate to Herod in haste they departed.
" This fine tall man—with what do you charge Him,
Finding it meet so straitly to guard Him?"

" He says He's the Son of the God that's in heaven."
" If that be the charge, I hereby condemn Him.

" Tie Him to the pillar till the twelfth hour to-morrow,
Bandage His eyes, a fool's robe for Him borrow.

" With hard ropes of hemp let ye tie Him and bind Him,
Spit in His face, mock Him and deride Him.

" Let every man strike Him—the Only Son of Mary,
Hie ye to the Garden, fell the largest tree therein.

" Bind Him to the Cross to suffer His Passion,
Drive the nails through His palms and show no compassion."

They hoisted Him up full high on their shoulders,
And then cast Him down on the pathway so stony.

" 'Tis time", said the Virgin, " to seek my Beloved."
Her hair was unbound and her feet were uncovered,
As His blood was a-shedding each droplet she gathered.

She burst through the guard and stood weeping before Him.
" Son, dost Thou not know the Mother that bore Thee?"
" Be patient, and God in due time will reward thee."

" Child, heavy Thy burden, Thy Mother should share it."
" For the sake of mankind I promised to bear it.
Mother, let everyone bear his own burden."

When the Jews heard these words they rushed forward to hold her,
They hoisted her up full high on their shoulders,
And then cast her down on the pathway so stony.

" If God's Son He be, He will raise up His Mother."
And straightway He raised up His Mother before them.

On the hard cruel Tree full high they then nailed Him,
On taking Him down He was bloodless and wasted.
" Look to Him now, 'tis for you to bewail Him."

" Alas! " said Saint Brigid, " He's only a wraith now,
Find the three Marys that they may bewail Him."
The three angels came and they made lamentation.

For their Father and His Mother the first lamentation,
The second they made for all human creation,
The third for impenitents doomed to damnation.

" That's the Virgin's lament, to be sung with deep feeling.
There's not one among you who knows it completely,

Chanting it daily, at morning or even,
Whom my Son will not welcome at last into heaven."
DONAL O'SULLIVAN

1. The lament of the Virgin for her Only Son. The three kings, if they were to come together, [would say]:

2. " If we should see Him again we would ask His pardon, So that we might obtain from Him forgiveness for our sins,

3. As did Mary Magdalen, And the woman who rubbed Him with the cloth (Veronica),

4. Or the woman who suffered for three years from a mysterious fever, Who found health and grace at the same instant,

5. Or the blind man who thrust the spear through His right side So that he beheld His blood spurt out in a stream,

6. And said that every drop of it was worth hundreds, Or the black thief that was on His right hand."

7. " My Child must go to the Garden to-morrow, Bringing the Book of the Passion in His hand."

8. " Summon the Apostles to Me that I may read them the Passion." " Lord," said Peter, " I will never part from Thee." " Verily, thy lips will deny Me thrice before to-morrow."

9. Dark Judas came, he gave Him a kiss and shook His hand. " Accursèd Judas, it is enough that thou hast sold Me without delivering Me into their hands."

10. They bound Him up with hard hempen ropes, They brought Him with them to Pilate, who gave Him a respite.

11. " What is your charge against this fine tall man, Whom you have surrounded with a guard such as this? "

12. " He says that He is the chief King of the Jews, and that grace is with Him." " If that is your charge against Him, I wash my hands of Him."

13. They bore Him with them to Herod without delay. " What is your charge against this fine tall man, Whom you have surrounded with a guard such as this? "

14. " He says that He is the Son of God and that grace is with Him." " According to my judgement it is a charge worthy of death.

15. " Bind Him to the pillar until the twelfth hour to-morrow, Put a bandage on His eyes and a fool's garment on Him.

16. " Bind Him up with hard hempen ropes, Spit on Him and mock Him.

17. " Let every man strike Him—the Only Son of Mary. Go to the Garden and cut the greatest tree that grows there.

18. " Put Him on the Cross to suffer the extreme Passion, Put the sharp nails ruthlessly through the palms of His hands."

19. They lifted Him up high on their shoulders And threw Him down on the hard stones of the street. " It is time for me ", said the Virgin, " to go seek my bright love."

20. Her hair was unbound and she was barefoot, As she was collecting His blood above the growing grass.

21. She leapt in and out of the guard: " God be with Thee, Son, dost Thou recognize Thy Mother? " " Be patient and thou wilt receive grace."

22. " Child, Thy load is great, let Thy Mother share it." " I promised to bear it for Adam's seed: Let each bear his own cross, Mother."

23. When the Jews heard these words being said by them, They hoisted her up high on their shoulders And threw her down on the hard stones of the street.

24. " Verily, if He be the Son of God He will raise up His Mother." Then He raised her up miraculously.

25. They raised Him up to the Cross of the Passion, And cast Him down as a poor heap of bones. " There He is for you now, and weep your fill over Him."

26. " O! truly," said Saint Brigid, " He is now nothing but a shadow. Where are the three Marys till they lament my bright love? " The three angels came and wept mournfully over Him.

27. They wept first for their Father and His Mother, The second time for Adam's race, And the third time for the sinner who never returns to Him.

28. " That is the lament of the Virgin; provided it be very sorrowful, Any of you who knows this chant,

29. " And who will say it, reciting it daily, My Son will not see Him condemned for ever."

The preceding three songs being literary products, their form and style inescapably belong to literature. In sharp contrast, the Lament of the Virgin emanates purely from the folk, and it contains no word that is not part of the speech of everyday life. Again, the sentiments of the other songs are those of the poets who wrote them; but the sentiments of this Lament and of others like it (for similar pieces are still on the lips of Irish speakers) may fairly be taken to be the sentiments of the community as a whole. In this age of scepticism and unbelief it is a remarkable and comforting thought that in one part of the Christian world the simple faith of the people shines so bright and so clear as to make the tremendous fact of Calvary part of their habitual mental climate, even representing Saint Brigid ("The Mary of the Gael") as being present at the Crucifixion. Similar laments were probably widespread in the Middle Ages. Italian folk laments of the same general type, in which Our Lord speaks to His Mother, will be found for instance in Paolo Toschi's *La Poesia Religiosa del Popolo Italiano* (Firenze, 1921, p. 36 *et seq.*).

I have been unable to translate this piece into rhymed verse without marring its essential simplicity. Instead, I have sought to provide an assonance roughly corresponding to the original. The lines are printed as couplets or triplets (according to the sense) for convenience of reading, but the entire Lament is sung without a break, each line being followed by the burden "*Och ochón! agus ochón Ó!*" meaning "Alas, alas and alas!" The chant-like tune is unlike anything known to me in Irish folk music. Both the tune and the words are doubtless very old.

The three Marys mentioned towards the end are the three named in St. John's Gospel (XIX, 25): "Now there stood by the cross of Jesus, his mother, and his mother's sister Mary of Cleophas, and Mary Magdalen." The three angels are probably the archangels Michael, Gabriel and Raphael.

DRINKING SONGS

The eighteenth century was supremely the age of convivial drinking, whether in the mansion, the farmhouse or the tavern. The well-to-do drank the wines of France, Portugal and Spain: particularly sherry, so that references to *fíon Spáinneach* (Spanish wine) are frequent in the songs of the poets and harpers who were their guests. In addition, most of the Big Houses brewed ale for their own use. The poor were fond of a heady type of ale called *lionn Márta* (March beer), which I think was made from heather and which is also mentioned in some of the songs; and they drank brandy when they could get it.

But the national drink of Ireland, of rich and poor alike, was of course whiskey, just as it is to-day. A serviceable still could be made for as little as five pounds, and there were thousands of them in the country. The excise duty (when people bothered to pay it at all) was trifling, being at one time a mere twopence per proof gallon; and the cost of John Barleycorn was amazingly low. In 1729 the price of a gallon of proof spirit in the open market was only one shilling and eightpence; and ten gallons of the finest *uisge beatha*, flavoured with cinnamon, mace, cloves and raisins, could be made for less than three pounds.

But if liquid refreshment was abundant and cheap, it was not reckoned more important than good conversation, music and song, the merry quip, the cut and thrust of argument. True conviviality was no less common in the cottage than in the hall, and if Carolan's song for Kean O'Hara speaks for the one Dick Barrett's "Another Round!" may be allowed to speak for the other. Indeed, John O'Toomey, the innkeeper-poet of Croom, County Limerick, went so far as to paint on his sign-board a rhymed invitation to all who might contribute to the evening's entertainment:

> Níl fánach gan fáltas ar uaisle Gaoidheal,
> Bráthair den dáimh glic nó suairc-fhear groí,
> I gcás go mbeadh láithreach gan luach na dighe,
> Nach mbeidh fáilte ag Seán geal Ó Tuama roí!

We might render it like this:

> There's no penniless stroller that springs from the Gael,
> A wit or a maker of rhyme or of tale,
> If he hasn't the money to pay on the nail,
> Still O'Toomey will welcome him here without fail!

Of course there is another side to the picture. Excessive indulgence in strong waters may have the unfortunate results suggested in some of the songs which follow; but the matter must be considered in the setting of the times. The odd word "teetotal" had not then been coined, and Irish Gaelic poets seemed naturally to take to drink—just as some drinkers took to poetry. Both classes were doubtless in cordial agreement with the sentiment of Byron's lines:

> Man, being reasonable, must get drunk :
> The best of life is but intoxication.

Hence when men like Barrett and Gunn are inclined to moralize on the subject, the unco' guid (who, like the poor, are always with us) ought not to complain if they seem to draw the wrong moral. Their attitude to any such would have been in the spirit of Sir Toby's retort to Malvolio: "Dost thou think, because thou art virtuous, there shall be no more cakes and ale?"

PREAB SAN ÓL! ANOTHER ROUND!

Is iomdha slí do bhíos ag daoine
  A' cruinniú píosaí 's a' déanamh stóir,
'S a luíod a smaoiníos ar ghiorra an tsaoil seo,
  'S go mbéidh siad sínte faoi leac go fóill.
Má's tighearna tíre, diúic nó rí thú,
  Ní cuirfíor pínn leat a' dul faoi'n bhfód:
Mar sin 's dá bhrí sin níl beart níos críonna
  Ná bheith go síorruí 'cur preab san ól!

An ceannuí craosach níl meón ná slí ar bith
  Le ór a dhéanamh nach bhfeicthear dhó,
An ráta is daoire ar an earra is saoire,
  Is ar luach shé bpíne go gcuirfeadh cróin.
Do réir chaint Chríosta is ní do-dhéanta
  An cámhall cíocrach a thabhairt thríd a' gcró:
Mar sin 's dá bhrí sin níl beart níos críonna
  Ná bheith go síorruí 'cur preab san ól!

An long ar sáile níl clúid ná ceárd
  I nach gcaithfeadh cáirde ar feadh an domhain mhóir,
Ó ríocht na Spáinne suas Gibráltar,
  Agus ansan áit a mbíonn an Grand Seigniór.
Le gach cárgo líonfadh málaí
  Ní choinneódh an bás uaidh uair ná ló:
Mar sin, a cháirde, níl beart níos fearr dhúinn
  Ná bheith mar tá sin, 'cur preab san ól!

Why spend your leisure bereft of pleasure
  Amassing treasure? Why scrape and save?
Why look so canny at every penny?
  You'll take no money within the grave!
Landlords and gentry, for all their plenty,
  Must still go empty—where'er they're bound:
So to my thinking we'd best be drinking,
  Our bumpers clinking in round on round!

The huxter greedy will grind the needy,
  Their straits unheeding, shouts " Money down! "
His special vice is his fancy prices,
  For a florin's value he'll charge a crown.
With hump for trammel the scripture's camel
  Missed the needle's eye and so came to ground:
Why pine for riches while still we've stitches
  To hold our breeches?—Another round!

The shipman trading to Spain or Aden
  Returns well laden with oil and corn,
Or from Gibraltar his course he'll alter
  And steer for Malta and the Golden Horn.
With easy motion he sails life's ocean,
  And ne'er a notion he'll soon go aground:
So, lads and lasses, because life passes,
  Let's fill our glasses for another round!

117

Is gearr a' saol tá ag a' lili sgiamhach,	King Solomon's glory, so famed in story,
Cé gur buí agus gur geal a góil,	Was far outshone by the lily's guise;
Agus Solamh críonna ina chulaí ríoghmhail	But hard winds harden both field and garden,
Nach bhfuil baol air i n-áille dhó.	Pleading for pardon the lily dies.
Níl sa' tsaol seo ach mar sionán gaoithe,	Life's but a bubble of toil and trouble,
Gath a sgaoiltear nó slám dho cheó:	A feathered arrow—once shot, ne'er found:
Mar sin 's dá bhrí sin níl beart níos críonna	It's nought but miming—so ends my rhyming,
Ná bheith go síorruí 'cur preab san ól!	But still we've time for just one last round!
RIOCARD BAIRÉAD	DONAL O'SULLIVAN

1. People have many ways Of amassing wealth and making a fortune. Little they reflect on the brevity of this life And that presently they will be under a tombstone. If you are a landlord, a duke or a king, You'll not take a penny with you going to the grave: Hence and for that reason there is no more sensible plan Than to be continuously drinking with spirit.

2. As for the covetous merchant, there is no means or method whatever Of making money that is not perceived by him: The dearest rate for the cheapest article, And for six pennyworth he'll charge a crown. According to Christ's saying it is a thing impossible For the greedy camel to pass through the eye of the needle: Hence and for that reason there is no more sensible plan Than to be continuously drinking with spirit.

3. The ship at sea, there is no corner or quarter In which it would not linger all over the world, From the kingdom of Spain down to Gibraltar, And in the place where the Grand Signior resides (the Sultan of Turkey). With all his bagfuls of cargo, He will not keep death from him for an hour or a day: Hence, friends, there is no better plan for us Than to be, as we are, continuously drinking with spirit.

4. Short is the life of the fair lily, Yellow and white though its dress be, And wise Solomon in his royal robes Could not rival it in beauty. This life is nothing but a puff of wind, A shot arrow or a wisp of mist: Hence and for that reason there is no more sensible plan Than to be continuously drinking with spirit.

Riocard Bairéad (Richard Barrett), the author of this fine convivial song, was born in 1739 at Belmullet, County Mayo, where he died in December, 1819. Schoolmaster by profession and poet by choice, he wrote a number of witty and satirical pieces, including "Owen Cóir", which will be found in the Historical Section (p. 155).

Barrett was a contemporary of the celebrated Irish advocate and orator John Philpot Curran (1750–1817); and the above poem bears certain resemblances to Curran's "The Deserter", which begins:

> If sadly thinking with spirits sinking
> Could more than drinking my cares compose,
> A cure for sorrow from sighs I'd borrow
> And hope to-morrow would end my woes.
> But since in wailing there's naught availing,
> And Death unfailing will strike the blow,
> Then for that reason and for a season
> Let us be merry before we go!

It will be seen that the metre and sentiment are the same, and the refrain of the one must be derived from the other. As Curran knew Irish and Barrett was well acquainted with English, the borrower might have been either.

The metre is not much used by English poets, though it is employed with ease and grace by Swinburne in his "Anima Anceps". But it is common enough in Irish and in popular Anglo-Irish songs with an Irish Gaelic basis, such as "The Groves of Blarney". In this connection it may be of interest to recall that Byron (who had met Curran at Holland House) also took the metre of "The Deserter" and adapted the refrain for one of his lyrics:

> Could Love for ever
> Run like a river,
> And Time's endeavour
> Be tried in vain—
> No other pleasure
> With this could measure,
> And like a treasure
> We'd hug the chain.

But since our sighing
Ends not in dying,
And, formed for flying,
    Loves plumes his wing,
Then for this reason,
Let's love a season,
But let that season
    Be only Spring.

Except for one slight change, Barrett does not vary the last two lines in any of his verses. As this may seem somewhat monotonous, I have ventured in my verse-rendering to provide different endings, within the spirit of the original.

A FHUISGÍ, CROÍ NA n-ANAMANN

WHY, LIQUOR OF LIFE, DO I LOVE YOU SO?

Giocoso

"A fhuis-gí, croí na n-an-am-ann, Leag-an tú ar lár me, Bím gan chéill, gan ai-thin-e, 'Sé an t-ach-a-rann dob fhearr liom! Bíonn mo chót-a strac-ai-the, 'Gus caill-im leat mo char-abh-at, Is bíodh a ndeár-nais mai-te leat, Ach teang-mhaigh liom a-már-ach!"

"Why, li-quor of life, do I love you so, When in all our en-count-ers you lay me low? More stu-pid and sense-less I ev-'ry day grow— What a hint, if I'd mend by the warn-ing! Tat-tered and torn you've left my coat, I've not a crav-at to save my throat, Yet I par-don you all, my spark-ling doat, If you'll cheer me a-gain in the morn-ing!"

(Pótaire)
" A fhuisgí, croí na n-anamann,
   Leagann tú ar lár me,
Bím gan chéill, gan aithine,
   'Sé an t-acharann dob fhearr liom!
Bíonn mo chóta stracaithe,
'Gus caillim leat mo charabhat,
Is bíodh a ndeárnais maite leat,
   Ach teangmhaigh liom amárach! "

(Toper)
" Why, liquor of life, do I love you so,
   When in all our encounters you lay me low?
More stupid and senseless I every day grow—
   What a hint, if I'd mend by the warning!
Tattered and torn you've left my coat,
I've not a cravat to save my throat,
Yet I pardon you all, my sparkling doat,
   If you'll cheer me again in the morning! "

(Fuisgí)
" Nuair éistfidh tusa an t-Aifreann
   Is beidh do shailm ráite,
Déin-se ionad coinne liom
   Is teangmhaigh liom i dtigh 'n táirne,
Mar a bhfeicfir cáirt is cnagaire,
Is coc i dtóin an bharraille,
Is bíodh an jar i n-aice leat,
   Is rót-sa chuirfead fáilte! "

(Whiskey)
" When you've heard prayers on Sunday next,
   With a sermon beside—or at least the text,
Come down to the ale-house, however you're vexed,
   And, though hundreds of cares assault you,
You'll find tippling there—till morals mend,
A cock shall be placed in the barrel's end,
The jar shall be near you, and I'll be your friend,
   And give you a céad míle fáilte! *"

(Pótaire)
" Och! mo stór is mo chara thú,
   Mo shiúr agus mo bhráthair,
Mo chúirt, mo thigh, mo thalamh thú,
   Mo chruach agus mo stáca!
Mo threabha, mo chéacht, mo chapaill thú,
Mo bha 's mo chaoire geala thú,
Is tar gach ní dár thagaras
   Do chongaibh mise páirt leat!

(Toper)
" You're my soul and my treasure, without and within,
   My sister, my cousin, and all my kin;
'Tis unlucky to wed such a prodigal sin,
   But all other enjoyment is vain, love!
My barley ricks all turn to you,
My tillage, my plough and my horses too;
My cows and my sheep, they have bid me adieu,
   I care not while you remain, love!

*A hundred thousand welcomes.

120

"Is iomdha bruíon is acharann
   Bhíodh eadrainn le ráithe,
Ach ní fhanann brón im aigne
   Nuair líontar chúm ar chlár thú!
Mo bhean agus mo leanbh thú,
Mo mháthair agus m'athair thú,
Mo chóta mór is mo *wrapper* thú,
   'S ní sgarfaidh mé go bráth leat!"

"Many's the quarrel and fight we've had,
   And many a time you have made me mad,
But while I've a heart it can never be sad
   When you smile at me full on the table!
For surely you are my wife and brother,
My only child, my father and mother,
My outside coat—I have no other,
   Oh! I'll stand by you while I'm able!"

JOHN D'ALTON

1. "Whiskey, heart of souls, You lay me low, I become senseless and unconscious, And fond of quarrelling! My coat is always tattered, And I have lost my cravat on your account, But may all you have done be forgiven So long as you'll meet me to-morrow!"

2. "When you will have heard Mass, And have said your psalm, Arrange a rendez-vous with me, And join me in the tavern, Where you will see a quart-pot and a noggin, And the bung at the bottom of the barrel, Place your jar within reach, And it's to yourself I'll give a welcome!"

3. "O! you are my love and my friend, My sister and my brother, My yard, my house, my land you are, My rick and my stack! My tillage, my plough and my horses you are, My cattle and my fair sheep you are, And in spite of all that I have mentioned I have kept my affection for you!

4. "Many's the quarrel and fight We have had this last quarter, But regret does not stay in my mind When you are filled for me at table! You are my wife and child, You are my mother and father, You are my great coat and my wrapper, And I will not part with you for ever!"

In his *Literary History of Ireland* (p. 599), Dr. Douglas Hyde ascribes this song to Carolan, for whom see pp. 180, 184; but the attribution must be considered doubtful. D'Alton's translation is not in the metre of the original but can nevertheless be sung to the tune.

TÁ 'N-A LÁ!　　　　　THERE'S THE DAY!

(Fear an táirne)

"Ó! chodlas féin i dtigh aréir,
　Is tuirseach tréith do bhí mo chuisle:
Comhrá béil bhí 'cu go léir,
　M'inghean féin 's a boc ar buile."

(Inghean agus Pótairí)

" Tá 'n-a lá!" " Níl 'n-a lá!"
　" Tá 'n-a lá agus 'n-a mhaidin!"
" Níl 'n-a lá, dheara, a ghrá,
　Ach solus árd atá sa' ghealaigh!"

(Pótaire)

"Éir' id shuí, 'fhir a' tighe,
　Cuir do bhríste 'mut go tapaidh,
Coinnigh suas cuideachta shuairc
　Don chroí mhaith mhór go dtiocfaidh an
　　mhaidean!"

(Fear an táirne)

" N'éireód im shuí," ar fear a' tighe,
　" 'S ní chuirfead bríste 'mum ná hata,
Blas ná braon dem chuid-se dighe
　A raghaidh na gcroí go dtiocfaidh an
　　mhaidean!"

(Pótaire)

" Tá mo stocaí i dtigh an óil,
　Tá mo bhróga i dtigh an leanna,
Tá mo bha a' dul thar teóirainn,
　Is níl bean óg a raghadh dá gcasa!"

(Innkeeper)

" A fitful sleep was mine last night,
　'Mid din and chat not of my choosing,
My daughter till the morning light
　Upbraiding those who sat there boozing."

(Daughter and Topers)

" There's the day!" " It's not the day!"
　" It is the day, the night is over!"
" It's not the day, whate'er you say,
　But the moonbeams bright to light the rover!"

(Toper)

" Come, landlord, join us in the snug,
　All drowsy thoughts of slumber scorning;
There's not a drop in jar or jug
　That we won't drain before the morning!"

(Innkeeper)

" I'll stop in bed," the landlord said,
　" Though if I don't you'll go out quicker!
Take your fill of swipes and swill,
　But not a gill of my good liquor!"

(Toper)

" The shebeen has my socks and shoes,
　The tavern has my coat and breeches;
By daybreak I'll have nought to lose—
　And then I'll snooze among the ditches!"

(Pótaire eile)
" Tá an barraille thar a cheann,
   Is ní fheicim ann ach dríodar dearga,
   Tá mo ghiní ar an mbórd,
      Is bíom ag ól go dtiocfaidh an mhaidean! "

(Another toper)
" I still can lend to treat a friend,
      And here's my guinea on the table;
   So tilt the barrel on its end,
      And let's be drinking while we're able! "

DONAL O'SULLIVAN

1. " I slept in a house last night, Tired and feeble was my arm: They were all arguing together, My own daughter and her buck in a rage."

Chorus. " Now it is day! " " It isn't day! " " It is the day and the morning! " " It isn't day, indeed, my love, But the high light of the moon! "

2. " Get up, man of the house, Put on your breeches quickly, Keep the jolly party going For the [man with a] great good heart till morning comes! "

3. " I won't get up," said the man of the house, " And I won't put on either breeches or hat. Not a taste or a drop of my liquor Will reach their hearts till morning comes! "

4. " My stockings are in the dram-shop, And my shoes are in the ale-house, My cows are breaking through the fences, And there's no young woman to head them off ! "

5. " The barrel is bottom upward, And I can see nothing inside it but reddish dregs, My guinea is on the counter, And let us be drinking till morning! "

AN BUACHAILL CAOL DUBH   THE DARK SLENDER BOY

Nuair a théim ar aonach a' ceannach éadaigh, 'S bíonn an
When I go to market to make a purchase And grasp the

éir-nis ag-am im láimh, Sín-eann taobh liom an
ear-nest with-in my hand, The dark slim lad-die still

buach-aill caol dubh, 'S cuir-eann caol-chrobh is-teach im láimh.
seeks and search-es Till he slips be-side me sed-ate and bland.

Is gearr 'n-a dhéidh sin go mbím go h-aer-ach, Gan puinn dem
It's not long aft-er my sense-less laugh-ter Will reach the

chéill 's mé os cionn an chláir, A' díol na n-éil-eamh do
raf-ter and I'm left prone; When I pay what's ow-ing, e'en

bhíonn am chéas-a, Seacht mí gan léin-e 's an fuacht am chrá.
though it's snow-ing, Quite bare I'm go-ing, my mon-ey gone.

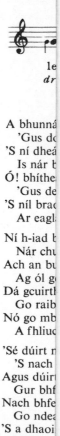

Nuair a théim ar aonach a' ceannach éadaigh
  'S bíonn an éirnis agam im láimh,
Síneann taobh liom an buachaill caol dubh,
  'S cuireann caol-chrobh isteach im láimh.
Is gearr 'n-a dhéidh sin go mbím go h-aerach,
  Gan puinn dem chéill 's mé os cionn an chláir,
A' díol na n-éileamh do bhíonn am chéasa,
  Seacht mí gan léine 's an fuacht am chrá.

'Sé an buachaill caol dubh fada, féileach,
  Clisde, léigheanta, 's gur mhaith é a shnó,
Do chlaoidh i bpéin mé 's do mhill i n-éag mé,
  Is d'fhág mé féinig ar beagán stóir.
Dhon Fhrainnc dá dtéinn, nó go cuan Binn Éadain,
  Nó a' dul don léim sin go h-Inis Mór,
Bíonn an séithleach im dhiaidh ar saothar,
  Mara mbeinn féin uaidh ach uair de ló.

When I go to market to make a purchase
  And grasp the earnest within my hand,
The dark slim laddie still seeks and searches
  Till he slips beside me sedate and bland.
It's not long after my senseless laughter
  Will reach the rafter and I'm left prone;
When I pay what's owing, e'en though it's snowing,
  Quite bare I'm going, my money gone.

The dark slim laddie's aye open-handed,
  So kind, so candid, with features fine;
But he has left me in pain, bereft me
  Of all my fortune, my sheep and kine.
If I took a notion to cross the ocean
  His deep devotion would not despair;
Swift as a swallow my track he'd follow,
  And on the morrow I'd find him there!

Do casadh Aoibhill na Craige Léith' orrainn,
  A' gabháil na slí is do ghaibh liom báidh;
Is dúirt dá ngéillfeadh an buachaill caol dubh
  Go dtúrfadh céad fear dó suas im áit.
Do labhair an caol-fhear go gonta géar lé,
  Is dúirt ná tréigfeadh a charaid ghnáth,
Gur shiúil sé Éire tré choillte 's réitigh
  Le cumann cléibh is le searc im dheáidh.

SEÁN AERACH Ó SEANACHÁIN

The Queen of Thomond met us while roaming
  Along the roadway and told the lad
If he'd me abandon that she would grant him
  A hundred topers to make him glad.
The slim boy answered in tones of banter
  'Twas ne'er his fancy to lose a friend:
O'er hill, o'er hollow he'd always follow
  A soak so mellow until the end!

DONAL O'SULLIVAN

1. When I go to the fair to buy cloth And have the earnest-money in my hand, The dark slender boy sidles up to me And slips his slender fingers within my hand. Shortly after that I become light-headed, Without a grain of sense as I lie over the counter; It is paying the reckoning that leaves me tormented, Seven months shirtless, and perished with the cold.

2. The dark slender boy is tall and festive, Clever and learned, of comely mien; 'Tis he who has afflicted me and ruined me for life, And left me impoverished. If I were to go to France or the harbour of Howth, Or thence at a bound to Inishmore, The wretch would come panting after me, Were I to be away from him for a single hour in the day.

3. Aoibhill* of the Grey Rock met us As we were going the road and she took a liking for me; And she said that if the dark slender boy would give me up She would give him a hundred men instead of me. The slim man spoke to her bluntly and forcibly, And said that he would not desert his boon companion: That he had travelled Ireland across hill and dale With heartfelt love and affection after me.

In this song we have the unusual and attractive concept of the Spirit of Drink as a Dark Slender Boy who accompanies his protégé everywhere. The author of the conceit was a Munster poet of the mid-eighteenth century named Seán Ó Seanacháin (John Shanahan), whose eccentric character and general irresponsibility earned for him the sobriquet of "Seán Aerach" or "Flighty Jack". According to the account given by O'Curry to Petrie, he was a native of Tulla, County Clare, who settled down in the neighbourhood of Glin, on the estuary of the Shannon in County Limerick.

Aoibhill, mentioned in the third verse, was the Fairy Queen of Thomond in Irish mythology; and her palace, Carraig Liath or The Grey Rock, is a hill overhanging the Shannon about a mile and a half above Killaloe, on the Clare side of the river. She appeared to Brian Boru on the battlefield of Clontarf (1014), predicted the outcome of the battle and informed the king of his impending death.

*Pronounced *Eevil*.

127

Ireland is noted for the variety and quality of its patriotic songs in English. "The Wearing of the Green", for example, is famous throughout the English-speaking world, and there are many others scarcely less well known: "The Shan Van Vocht", "The Minstrel Boy", "The Harp That Once", "The Rising of the Moon", "Who Fears To Speak of 'Ninety-Eight?", "The West's Asleep", "God Save Ireland!", and so on, the most recent being "A Soldier's Song", which has been adopted as the national anthem. Great though the merits of many of them be, these are all utterly alien from the thought and spirit of the Irish-speaking Ireland with which this book deals. Few were written to native tunes, and one and all are the product of that English mentality which, with the decay of the Irish tongue, began to permeate the common people at the outset of the nineteenth century, waxed strong after the Famine, and was all but universal by the time of the rise of the Home Rule movement under Parnell. The world of difference between such songs and those of the Gaelic poets becomes painfully evident when, as sometimes happens, they are translated into Irish. However competent the translations, the effect is as unnatural and uninspired as, say, the French version of Kipling's *Barrack Room Ballads*.

Patriotic songs in Irish are nothing like so common as those in English, because the mind of the Irish-speaking people did not work in that way. Also, the number of types is far fewer, the main reason being the predominance of the *aisling* or vision, of which "The Mower" is a specimen and the structure of which is described in the note to that song. For the rest, the poet (known or unknown) took a familiar tune—usually that of a love song— and composed patriotic words to it. The name of the girl in the love song was retained, because (if for no other reason) it provided a ready indication of the tune to which the new words were intended to be sung; and this name is applied in allegorical fashion to Ireland. Hence we get such synonyms as Caitilín Ní Uallacháin, Gráinne Mhaol, Cáit Ní Dhuibhir, Síle Ní Ghadhra and Caitilín Triall, the English forms of which would be (oddly as they sound in English) Kathleen Houlihan, Granuaile, Kate O'Dwyer, Sheila O'Gara and Kathleen Tyrrell. There is nothing romantic in all this, and the choice of names is quite fortuitous. It is still sometimes alleged that the device was employed as a disguise in view of the penal laws, but to anyone able to read Irish the assertion is nonsensical. The poets placed no restraint whatever on the expression of their views about the English, as the reader will see from the songs in the present section and in the historical section which follows.

Says the leading character in W. B. Yeats's great play: "Some call me the Poor Old Woman, and there are some that call me Cathleen, the daughter of Houlihan"; and it is possible that this single sentence has gained more converts for Irish nationalism than anything written in our time. We may freely concede that the concept of Ireland as a Poor Old Woman (Shan Van Vocht) is beautiful and touching, but it was certainly not intended to be so in its inception. At the close of the eighteenth century there was a popular song in Irish, of a scurrilous type, dealing with the unpleasant theme of a young man married to an old woman. The title, which also figured in the burden, was "*Sean-Bhean Bhocht*" ("Shan Van Vocht" or "Poor Old Woman"). The fleet of the French Directory was then threatening invasion, and an anonymous song in English was composed to the tune, with the old refrain:

> O! the French are on the sea,
> Says the Shan Van Vocht,

and so on. Prior to the presumed date of that song, there is no trace in Irish or Anglo-Irish literature of any such allegorical conception. It is, in fact, due to the accidental adoption of the older song with this burden as a new vehicle for popular emotion.

I have stated, or implied, that the Gaelic poets were not specially attracted to the patriotic theme. In this connection the reader unacquainted with Irish should be warned that the translators, possibly feeling the absence of the patriotic note to be a defect, sometimes supplied it themselves. Thus, in "The Fair Hills of Éire O!" (p. 91) Mangan writes:

> Far dearer unto me than the tones music yields
> Is the lowing of the kine and the calves in her fields,
> And the sunlight that shone long ago on Gaelic shields
> On the fair hills of Éire O!

But the original makes no mention of the Gaelic shields of long ago; it merely speaks (far more poetically) of the sunlight falling on old and young. Again, in his rendering of "John O'Dwyer of the Glen" (p. 147) Sigerson has:

> We hear no joyous shouting
> From the blackbird brave,

obviously alluding to the Young Pretender, who was allegorically called "The Blackbird" and who enters the picture more than a century after the poem was written. All that O'Dwyer says is that, owing to the razing of the forests, the thrush and the blackbird will be heard no more.

RÓISÍN DUBH   THE SMALL BLACK ROSE

Andante

A — Róis - ín, ná bíodh brón ort ná — cás a -
My — Rose, do not — mourn for — what has hap - pened

- nois, Tá do phár - dún ón — Róimh is — ón bPáp - a
thee, The — friars are draw-ing nigh - er — from a - cross the

'gam, Tá na brái - thre 'teacht thar sáil - e — 's a' triall — thar
sea, Rome's par - don for my darl - ing will ease — her

muir, — 'S ní ceil - fear fíon Spáinn - each ar mo Róis - ín Dubh!
woes, And wine from Spain salve the pain of — my — Small Black Rose!

A Róisín, ná bíodh brón ort
    ná cás anois,
Tá do phárdún ón Róimh is
    ón bPápa agam,
Tá na bráithre 'teacht thar sáile
    is a' triall thar muir,
Is ní ceilfear fíon Spáinneach
    ar mo Róisín Dubh!

Is fada an réim do thug mé féin
    ó 'né go 'niu,
I n-imeall sléibh' 'muigh go h-innealt' éadtrom,
    mar b'eólach dom;
Loch Éirne do léimeas,
    cé gur mór é a sruth,
'S gan im dhéidh mar ghile gréine
    ach mo Róisín Dubh!

Tá grá agam im lár dhuit
    le bliain anois,
Grá cráite, grá cásmhar,
    grá cíapaithe,
Grá d'fhág mé gan sláinte,
    gan rian, gan ruith,
Is go bráth bráth gan aon fháil agam
    ar mo Róisín Dubh!

Do shiúlfainn-se an Mhumhain leat
    is ciumhais na gcnoc,
Mar shúil go bhfaghainn rún ort
    nó páirt le cion.
A chraobh chumhartha, tuigtear dhúinn-ne
    go bhfuil grá agat dom,
'S gurab í plúr-sgoth na mban múinte
    mo Róisín Dubh!

My Rose, do not mourn for
    what has happened thee,
The friars are drawing nigher
    from across the sea,
Rome's pardon for my darling
    will ease her woes,
And wine from Spain salve the pain of
    my Small Black Rose!

Long my faring throughout Erin
    since yester night,
Lough Erne in my yearning
    I leapt outright;
Over highways and byways
    the pilgrim goes,
Aflame with the name of
    my Small Black Rose!

I adore thee, watch o'er thee
    the livelong year,
With no guerdon for love's burden
    but black despair;
With spirits pining, health declining,
    my passion grows,
Yet vainly I strive to gain thee,
    my Small Black Rose!

I'd roam in the gloaming
    through Munster's plain,
Over hill side and by rill side
    her heart to gain;
She is fairer, far rarer,
    than any flower that blows,
Is she yielding to my pleading,
    my Small Black Rose?

Beidh an fhairrge 'n-a tuilte dearga 's an spéir 'n-a fuil, Beidh an saol 'n-a choga craorac do dhruim na gcnoc. Beidh gach gleann sléibh' ar fuid Éireann is móinte ar crith, Lá éigin sul a n-éagfaidh mo Róisín Dubh!	The sea's flood will be blood-red, the sky aflame, The whole world will be hurled into ruin and shame, Hills will tremble and crumble in agony's throes, Ere the day that death takes thee, my Small Black Rose!

DONAL O'SULLIVAN

1. O little Rose, grieve not now nor repine, I have your pardon from Rome and from the Pope, The friars are coming across the sea and faring o'er the main, And Spanish wine will not be hidden from my Small Black Rose!

2. Long is the journey that I took from yesterday until to-day, Out on the confines of the mountains, light and limber as I knew how; I leapt Lough Erne, great though its expanse be, With no sunbeam in my wake but my Small Black Rose!

3. I have loved you from my heart now for a twelvemonth, An anguished love, a hapless love, a love tormented, A love that has left me without health, without vigour, without activity, And for evermore I cannot win my Small Black Rose!

4. I would travel Munster with you and the borders of the hills, In hope to gain your affection and your loving friendship. O fragrant branch, I feel that you love me, And the fine flower of gentle women is my Small Black Rose!

5. The sea will be turned to red floods and the sky to blood, The world be in crimson battle on the ridges of the hills, Every mountain valley throughout Ireland, every bog will quake, One day ere shall die my Small Black Rose!

I have included this impassioned lyric among the patriotic songs because it has long been so regarded, giving to us in *"Róisín Dubh"* the most beautiful of all the poetical names for Ireland. There is no doubt that, like others of its type, it originated as a love song to which the second, third and fourth verses perhaps belong, though they might also be construed in an allegorical sense. But the last verse seems clearly to have a patriotic meaning and no other.

As to the opening verse, O'Curry remarks: "The parties must have been within the forbidden degrees of relationship, or the woman restrained by particular vows. Cases of both kinds are to be found in our history and have been, for a long time at least, dependent on a papal dispensation for their final issue. And the allusion to this fact here is so clear that it requires no argument to prove it." This seems to me to be an odd, humorless and wholly untenable judgement. The writer of a love poem does not announce in it to his affianced bride that the legal and religious formalities have now been satisfactorily settled, and a "pardon" is not the same thing as a dispensation or a marriage licence. The song probably dates from the seventeenth century (Hardiman puts it as early as the Rebellion of Red Hugh O'Donnell under Elizabeth); and the allusion in these opening lines—admittedly obscure—may well be to the hoped-for triumph of the Catholic Church in Ireland, with the support of Spain.

"Róisín Dubh" has already been rendered three times into English verse—by Thomas Furlong, Edward Walsh and James Clarence Mangan. Unfortunately, none of these translations is in the exact metre of the original and so I have been obliged to attempt another, claiming no special merit for it except that it can be sung to the tune. In addition to translating the poem, Mangan was inspired by it to write his incomparable "Dark Rosaleen".

Con moto

Mo léan le lua 'gus m'at-uir-se! 'S ní féar do bhuain ar teas-cann-aibh D'fhúig
A - las! a - lack! and well - a - day! 'Tis not the task of mow-ing hay Has

céas-ta buar-tha m'aig-in-e Le tréimh-se go tláth, Ach
left my mind so sad to-day, De - ject-ed and sore, But the

éig-se's suadh-a'n tsean-a-chais I ngéibh-eann chruaidh's i n-an-ac-ra, Go
thought of those I hold most dear, The bard and sage in bond-age drear, Des-

tréith i dtua-thaibh lea-than-Luirc Gan réim mar ba ghnáth.
-pised and mocked both far and near On Er-in's green shore.

Is gach lon-na-bhil-e bor-ab-chu-thaigh tréan-chum-ais d'fhás De
And the no-ble band of he-roes grand whose fath-ers came from Spain, That

bhrol-la-stoc na son-a-chon do phréamh-uigh ón Spáinn Go
on the field would nev-er yield but proud-ly fought a-main, By

cann-tlach faon-lag eas-bui-theach, Fá ghall-smacht ghéar ag dan-ar-aibh, An
treach-'rous wiles of knav-er-y All sunk in dark-est slav-er-y, Their

cam-sprot claon do sheal-a-bhuigh A saor-bhail-te stáit!
lands, their homes, once fair and free, Now know them no more!

Mo léan le lua 'gus m'atuirse!
'S ní féar do bhuain ar teascannaibh
D'fhúig céasta buartha m'aigine
    Le tréimhse go tláth,
Ach éigse 's suadh' an tseanachais
I ngéibheann chruaidh 's i n-anacra,
Go tréith i dtuathaibh leathan-Luirc,
    Gan réim mar ba ghnáth.
Is gach lonna-bhile borab-chuthaigh tréan-chumais d'fhás
De bhrolla-stoc na sona-chon do phréamhuigh ón Spáinn
    Go canntlach faon-lag easbuitheach,
    Fá ghall-smacht ghéar ag danaraibh,
    An cam-sprot claon do shealabhuigh
        A saor-bhailte stáit!

134

Go fann aréir 's mé 'machtnamh ar
Gach plannda 'en Ghaeal-fhuil chalama,
An drong ba thréin' i gceannas chirt
   'S i réim Inis Fáil,
Le feall-bheart chlaon is gangaid uilc
Gach samhairle 's sméirle Sasanaigh,
Go fallsa shéan an t-Aifireann
   Is saor-staid na ngrás,
I n-anacra, fá tharcuisne 's i ngéar-bhruidibh gáidh
Ag cama-shliocht na malluitheacht', an éithigh 's an smáil.
   Tré bhuairt an sgéil seo chealag sinn
   Go duairc, is léir, mar aithrisfead,
   Le suan-bhriocht tréith gur treasgradh mé
      Im thréan-chodla spás.

Trím néal ar cuaird 'sea dhearcas-sa
Réaltann uasal taitneamhach
Go béasach buacach ceannasach
   A' téarnamh im dháil:
Ba dhréimreach dualach daite tiugh
A craobh-fholt cuachach camarsach
A' téacht go sguabach bachalach
   Lé i n-éinfheacht go sáil.
'N-a leacain ghil, mar cheapaid draoithe, éigse 'gus fáidhe,
Gur sheasaimh Cúipid cleasach glic is gaethe 'n-a láimh,
   Ar tí gach tréin-fhir chalama
   Do thíodh 'n-a gaor do chealaga,
   Tré'r claoiodh na céadta faraire
      I ndaor-chreathaibh báis.

Ba bhinne séis a tana-ghuib
Ná fuinneamh méar a' spreaga puirt
'S ná cruit an té do threasgair Mis,
   Ciodh baoth dham a rá;
'S ba ghil' a h-éadan sneachtamhail
Ná'n lile caomh 's ná'n eala 'r sruth,
'S ba snuite caol a mala suit'
   Ar réalt-dhearc gan cháim;
A mama cruinne 'r sheanga-chruith nár léanadh le práisc,
A leabhar-chrobh do bheartadh luingeas, éanlaith is bláth;
   Ba mhíonla maordha maiseamhail
   A h-íor 's a sgéimh 's a pearsa-chruth,
   Do ghríosuigh mé chum labhartha
      'S na bréithribh seo im dheáidh:

"A ríoghan bhéasach, aithris dam
An tú an aoil-chnis tré n-ar treascaradh
Na mílt' 'en Fhéinn le gaisge Thailc
   Mhic Thréin thug an t-ár?
Nó'n bhrídeach Hélen d'aistirigh
Tar tuinn ón nGréig lér cailleadh truip
I *siege* na Trae mar bheartaid draoith'
   I léir-rannaibh dán?
Nó'n mhascalach ó Alabain thug laoch leis 'n-a bhárc,
An ainnir lér thuit clann' Uisnigh mar léightear san Táin?
   Nó'n ríoghan aerach thaithneamhach
   D'fhúig saoithe Gaeal i n-ana-bhruid,
   Dá druim gur phréamhuigh danair uilc
      I réim Inis Fáil?"

135

Is béasach stuamdha d'fhreagair mé,
'S í 'déanamh uaille 's cathuithe:
" Ní h-aon dár luais id starthaibh mé,
    Ciodh léir dam an táin.
'S mé céile 's nuachair Charoluis,
Tá déarach duairc, fé tharcuisne,
Gan réim ná bua mar chleachtas-sa,
    Mo laoch ó tá 'r fán.
Ach le feartaibh cirt an araid-Mhic fuair peannaid croise 's páis,
Beidh sgaipe 's rith ar Ghalla-phuic do shealabhuigh ár stát.
    Ní danaid liom an aicme thug
    Mo dhearca 'sile lachta tiugh
    I n-ana-bhruid fé'n ama 'ge
        Gach saor-bhile sámh.

" Fí mar luadar seana-dhraoithe
'Ríomhadh tuar is tarngaireacht,
Beidh flít i gcuantaibh Banaba
    Fá fhéile Shain Seáin,
A' túirt sgimhle 's ruag' a fearann Chuirc
Tar linntibh rua na faraige
Ar gach smísteach muar-chuirp Sasanaigh,
    'S ní léan liom a bpráinn.
Beidh gearra cloidhte 's sgaipe truip is tréan-treasgairt námhad
Ar gach ailp aca do chleachtadh *punch* is féasta san Pháis:
    Dob aite sult na reamhar-phoc
    A' cnead 's a' crith le h-eagala
    Ná'n reacaireacht so cheapadar
        Lucht féir-leaga 'r phá! "

EOGHAN RUA Ó SÚILLEABHÁIN

Alas! alack! and well-a-day!
'Tis not the task of mowing hay
Has left my mind so sad to-day,
    Dejected and sore,
But the thought of those I hold most dear,
The bard and sage, in bondage drear,
Despised and mocked both far and near
    On Erin's green shore.
And the noble band of heroes grand whose fathers came from Spain,
That on the field would never yield but proudly fought amain,
    By treacherous wiles of knavery
    All sunk in darkest slavery,
    Their lands, their homes, once fair and free,
        Now know them no more!

Yestreen I lay in pensive mood,
My thoughts on men of Gaelic blood,
The race that rightly held each rood
    Of famed Inisfáil,*
Now brought to such a grievous pass
By English whelps and thieves, alas!
The churls that falsely spurn the Mass,
    The priesthood, and all:
Now sore distressed, by grief oppressed, aye, hungry and athirst,
The wretched pawn of devil's spawn, by aliens accursed.
    As on our woes my thoughts I kept,
    With breaking heart salt tears I wept,
    Till magic slumber o'er me crept
        And held me in thrall.

*Pronounced *Innish-fall*

As in my dream I wandered far,
Upon my path I met a star,
More fair than earthly maidens are,
　　More gracious, more kind:
Her glossy tresses, flowing free
Like spume upon a troubled sea,
Came tumbling downward to her knee,
　　And streamed in the wind.
Upon her snood blithe Cupid stood, his quiver full of darts,
As poets tell, with intent fell to penetrate the hearts
　　Of all who, greatly venturesome,
　　To greet this lovely maid might come,
　　Whence heroes bold were stricken dumb,
　　　　To death were resigned.

Her gentle voice was soft and low,
Like harmonies of long ago
On harp or magic viol, though
　　'Tis wildly I speak:
Her skin the lily put to shame,
Her posture that of swan on stream,
Her chiselled brows a classic frame
　　For roses in cheek:
Her shapely breast still unconfessed to lovers who deceive,
Her fingers deft at warp and weft a tapestry would weave.
　　Emboldened by her gracious mien,
　　I ventured on the tranquil scene,
　　And modestly approached my queen,
　　　　Her lineage to seek.

"Art thou the lady whom to gain
Dread Tailc Mac Treóin† crossed o'er the main,
When thousands were in battle slain,
　　And died in their gore?
Or Helen fair, the Grecian bride,
Who, ravished to Scamander-side,
Brought down on Troy destruction's tide,
　　So famous in lore?
Or Deirdre frail who set her sail from Alba o'er the sea,
For whom were slain on Navan's plain the noble brothers three?
　　Or the light-o'-love called Dervorgill,
　　A name that history echoes still,
　　For 'twas through her that foreign ill
　　　　First touched on our shore?"

She answered me between her sighs,
But gently still, with limpid eyes,
" I'm none of those whom you surmise,
　　Famed though they be:
Behold in me the rightful Queen,
The spouse of Charles, though now, I ween,
You see in mine a tragic mien,
　　With my hero o'er sea.
But God is good and, by the rood on which He died for men,
He soon will chase the foreign race from out our land again.
　　I'll pity not the treacherous horde
　　When once they're smitten by the Lord,
　　My harp will sound a joyful chord,
　　　　For the Gaels will be free!

†*Tailc* pronounced as English *talc*, and *Treóin* as English *throne* without the *h.*

137

"As ancient seers and prophets tell,
Who con and read the omens well,
A fleet will brave the ocean swell
  On Saint John's Day;
From Munster's lands 'twill put to rout
Each portly, thieving English lout,
They'll one and all be driven out
  And swept far away.
The gleaming spears, the gun that sears, will banish them at last,
The greedy swine who swilled their wine and scorned the Friday fast.
  And when at last the Gaels arise,
  The music of the Saxon sighs
  Will bring more gladness to mine eyes
  Than the mower's sweet lay!"

DONAL O'SULLIVAN

1. My grief to mention, and my affliction! And it is not the journey-work of making hay That has left my mind troubled and in anguish And weak for a spell, But that the poets and learned men versed in history Are in sore bondage and in misery, Languid in the lands of mighty Lorc (Ireland), Shorn of their wonted power: And every ardent champion, fiercely wrathful, mighty in strength, that sprang From the genuine race of the chieftains that hailed from Spain, Sorrowful, a-weary, in want, Under the harsh foreign tyranny of the stranger, The treacherous rabble that took possession Of their free steadings.

2. Forspent last night I was meditating on Every scion of the staunch Gaelic blood, The race that was strongest in rightful authority And power in Inisfáil (Ireland): How, through the fell treachery and ill deceit Of the English whelps and thieves Who falsely denied the Mass And the free state of grace, They (the Gaels) are distressful, despised, experiencing the sharp pangs of want At the hands of the crooked spawn of iniquity, lying and sin. Through grief at the recital that wounded me Sorely, it is clear, as I shall tell, That I was overcome by a faint magical sleep, [And lay] in deep slumber awhile.

3. While in my dream I beheld approaching A noble and lovable lady, Mannerly, comely, of proud mien, Advancing to meet me. In long plaited tresses, glossy and thick, Her branching locks, curled and twisted, Reached in sweeping, ringletted masses All down to her heels. In her glowing cheeks, as the poets, bards and seers fancy, Playful, tricksy Cupid stood with darts in his hand, On the point of wounding Every hero that might venture near, Whence warriors were laid low by the hundred In the dread throes of death.

4. Sweeter the music of her slender lips Than nimble fingers making melody And than the harp of him who overcame Mish, Wildly though I speak; And her snowy countenance was whiter Than fair lily or than swan on stream, And delicately chiselled were her brows set Over faultless, starry eyes. Her round breasts on her lissom body were undefiled by wantonness, Her graceful hands could work ships, birds and flowers [on tapestry]. So gentle, sedate, so beautiful Her figure, her form and her person, That I was emboldened to speak In these words that follow.

5. "Gentle queen, tell me Are you the fair-skinned one (Niamh) who caused the overthrow Of thousands of the Fianna to whom Tailc Mac Treóin Brought slaughter by his feat of arms? Or the lady Helen that fared Overseas from Greece through whom a troop was lost In the siege of Troy as poets tell In well-remembered lays? Or the graceful one from Scotland (Deirdre) whom a hero carried off with him in his barque [And who was] the maid through whom fell the children of Uisneach, as we read in the saga? Or the lightsome, lovable queen (Dervorgilla) That left the Irish nobles desolate, Since through her the evil foreigners took root In the realm of Inisfáil (Ireland)?"

6. Kindly and demurely she answered me Between her tears and sobs: "I am none of those mentioned in your recital, Though I am familiar with all. I am the bride and spouse of Charles, Tearful, dejected and contemned, Shorn of my wonted power and dominion, Since my hero is in exile. Through the just miracles of the divine Son Who suffered the pains of the Cross and of the Passion, The foreign bucks who seized our state will be scattered and put to rout. I have no pity for the horde that made My eyes shed copious tears, [When they are] enslaved beneath the yoke of Each splendid free champion.

7. "According to the utterances of the ancient soothsayers, Who used to read omens and make prophecies, There will be a fleet in the bays of Banba (Ireland) By Saint John's Day, Routing and expelling from the lands of Corc (Munster), Across the red deeps of the sea, Every big-bodied English boor, And I gloat over their trepidation. There will be sword-slashing and troop-scattering and mighty, hostile overthrow For every stout, sleek man of them who was wont to feast and drink punch of a Friday. More joyous the sighing Of the fat bucks and their shaking with fear Than this poem that has been composed By hired harvesters!"

No collection of Irish patriotic songs would be complete without an *aisling* (pronounced *ashling*) or vision; for when the poets felt the urge to write this type of verse they almost always chose that form. The metre would of course vary, according to the tune—Irish, Scottish or English—that the poet had in mind; but the general theme remained unchanged and even the detail varied only within narrow limits.

The poet is reflecting on Ireland's woes when he falls asleep, or else he is wandering in some part of the countryside with his mind similarly occupied. A lady, surpassingly fair, appears to him in a vision. The beauty of her form, her features, her hair, all are minutely described. A usual metaphor is that the rose and the lily were struggling for mastery in her cheek, and mention is sometimes made of her skill in tapestry.

He asks her identity, suggesting the names of various Irish and classical goddesses or some *femme fatale* of mythology or history. She replies that she is none of these, but Ireland, occasionally representing herself, in allegorical fashion, as the spouse of the exiled Stuart king. She reviews her present woeful condition and predicts the early expulsion of the foreigner. On this note the vision ends. If the *genre* had been exploited to only a limited extent, the results would perhaps be valued more highly. But when one has read literally scores of such pieces it becomes a case of *crambe repetita*. ✗

In the above song, the women mentioned or alluded to (verse 5) are:

Niamh (Niav), who figures in the Ossianic lay called *Cath Chnuic an Áir* ("The Battle of the Hill of Slaughter"). Being promised in marriage to the repellent Tailc Mac Treóin, she fled for protection to the Fianna—the Irish warriors of legend. Tailc followed her to Ireland and slew many of the Fianna before being himself slain by Oscar, son of Oisín (Ossian). Niamh died of horror at the slaughter of which she had been the innocent cause.

Helen of Troy.

Deirdre, probably the most famous woman character in Gaelic mythology. Her romantic adventures with the three sons of Uisneach and their subsequent death form one of the tales called by the Irish "The Three Sorrows of Story telling". Plays have been written about her in our own day by W. B. Yeats, J. M. Synge and others.

Dervorgilla, wife of O'Rourke, Prince of Bréifne. In the year 1152 she was carried off by Dermot MacMurrough, King of Leinster. O'Rourke, with his friends and allies, invaded MacMurrough's territory and the latter sought the aid of Henry II of England. This brought about the first English invasion of Ireland in 1169.

There is a further mythological allusion, in verse 4, to "the harp of him who overcame Mis" (Mish). Mis is a frenzied woman of legend who held sway over the mountain-range of Sliabh Mis (Slieve Mish) in County Kerry, and who was restored to reason by the harp-music of Dubh Ruis, the harper of King Feidhlime. (*Celtica*, I, pp. 382–385 and II, pp. 325–333.)

"The Mower", a masterpiece of the *aisling* form, was written by Owen Rua O'Sullivan (1748–1784), of whom I have already given some account in the note to his "Farewell to Carraig an Éide" (p. 97). Of the circumstances in which it was written we know no more than can be gleaned from a laconic note in the manuscripts that the poet was working as a harvest-labourer at the time, on the banks of the Blackwater near Mallow, in County Cork. But this is perhaps a case in which we are entitled to use our imagination to some extent.

The day's mowing is over, and the harvesters are gathered for an evening's diversion in the spacious farmhouse kitchen, Owen among them: a stocky figure in his frieze coat and knee-breeches, the handsome, intellectual face somewhat out of harmony with a pair of hands that have been roughened and reddened by the scythe. There is ale for those who

Aisling.

call for it, and whiskey as well; and the night is spent in singing and story-telling, the gossip of the countryside and dancing with the girls.

There have been jigs, reels, set-dances, and now the fluter starts a hornpipe. The couples move to take the floor, but not Owen. He sits pensive in a corner by the turf fire, wondering where has he heard that captivating melody before. He remembers now. It was on the fo'c's'le deck of his ship as she lay in the Downs, the night before they set sail for the West Indies. The sailors were dancing to it clumsily, most of them three sheets in the wind, having spent their last shore-leave as sailors do.

A queer name it had too, if only he could recall it. Was it not—? Yes it, was! "Come ashore, Jacky Tar, with your trousers on!" He laughed to himself as he thought of the time they lay off Port Royal on the morrow of Rodney's victory over the French: how he swopped his working dress of short skirt and peaked cowl for his bell-bottomed trousers and round cap (number one rig, the English sailors called it) before taking the liberty-boat to meet the girls waiting on the steps at the end of the old mole. Good times, those were!

The music continues, but now his face grows graver beneath his flaming hair. What is making him so mind-weary and heart-sore? Not mowing to be sure, for he is used to physical labour and doesn't mind it. No, but the knowledge that he and his like—poets, men of learning, heirs of an ancient and honourable tradition—are condemned to a degraded existence by the tyrannical rule of the upstart and ignorant foreigner. And so, almost without conscious effort on his part, his thoughts shape themselves to the rhythm of the melody:

> *Mo léan le lua 'gus m'atuirse!*
> *'S ní féar do bhuain ar teascannaibh*
> *D'fhúig céasta buartha m'aigine*
> *Le tréimhse go tláth.*

. . . Before the dancers leave the floor, the first verse is complete in his mind, without the need for alteration of a single syllable: for this is a man who possesses the divine gift, so rare even among great lyrists, of wedding music and poetry. The evening's revelry over, he climbs the ladder to his shake-down in the loft, there to finish his vision with quill pen by the light of a guttering candle before retiring to rest; and when the next day's harvesting is finished all seven verses are ready to be sung to the assembled company.

CAITILÍN NÍ UALLACHÁIN   CATHLEEN NI HOULIHAN

Risoluto

Ó!___ meas-aim-íd nach cal-am rinn den___ bhuairt seo___
Think not like some that peace will come from this___ tur - moil___ in

'Spáinn, Ach meal-la slí___ chum cha-tha cloímh do___ thúirt___ i
Spain, 'Tis but a way to___ gain de-lay and join bat-tle a-

dtráth. Beidh Gall-a 'rís___ dá___ leag-a síos le___ lúth___ ár___
-gain. The for-eign foe___ will be yet laid low, our___ swords will be___

lámh, Is___ Mac an Rí ag___ Cait-il-ín Ní___ Uall___ ach-áin!
drawn, When the Prince is seen with Cath-al-een Ni___ Houl-i-han!

Ó! measaimíd nach calm rinn
    den bhuairt seo i Spáinn,
Ach mealla slí chum chatha cloímh
    do thúirt i dtráth.
Beidh Galla arís dá leaga síos
    le lúth ár lámh,
Is Mac an Rí ag Caitilín
    Ní Uallacháin!

Geallaim díbh nach fada arís
    gur buartha an gháir
Ag arm faoir dá gceapa linn
    is fuadar lámhaigh;
Is tapa cruinn do phreabfaimís
    's is buacach árd
Dá mbeadh Mac an Rí ag Caitilín
    Ní Uallacháin!

Is fada sinn a' faire arís
    le fuasgailt d'fháil,
'N-ár stallairí gan balcaisí
    ná a lua 'n-ár láimh.
Beidh barca líonta ar barra taoide
    is fuaim ar sáil
Le Mac an Rí chum Caitilín
    Ní Uallacháin!

Ná measaidís na spreallairí
    gur buan ár bpáis,
Is gur gearra bhíd na glasa a' sgaoile
    nuair is cruaidhe an cás.
Go ndearna Maois roimh phobal Ísrael
    den mhuar-mhuir tráigh,
Is go bhfóire Críost ort, a Chaitilín
    Ní Uallacháin!

LIAM DALL Ó hIFEARNÁIN

Think not like some that peace will come
    from this turmoil in Spain,
'Tis but a way to gain delay
    and join battle again.
The foreign foe will be yet laid low,
    our swords will be drawn
When the Prince is seen with Cathaleen
    Ni Houlihan!

Our hopes run high, the time is nigh
    for the hazard of war,
The plans are laid, the weapons made,
    the guns soon will roar.
While others sleep our watch we'll keep
    and proudly hail the dawn
When the Prince is seen with Cathaleen
    Ni Houlihan!

We're bowed with care, in black despair,
    downtrodden like slaves,
Ill-clad, ill-fed, without boots or bread,
    our dwellings in caves.
But a mighty fleet our Queen will greet
    as westward it speeds on,
And the Prince is seen with Cathaleen
    Ní Houlihan!

Our hated foes must ne'er suppose
    our doom is for aye,
Though the heavens are dark we still can mark
    God's arch in the sky.
As Moses led through the Ocean Red
    all Israel on,
So may Christ screen thee, Cathaleen
    Ni Houlihan!

DONAL O'SULLIVAN

1. We do not think that it is peace which this upheaval in Spain has become, But the cunning preparing of the way to bring about an opportune clash of arms. The foreigners will yet be laid low by the strength of our arm, And the King's Son shall return to Cathleen Ni Houlihan!

2. I promise you it will not be long now till the clamour will arise Of weapons being readied by us, and the intent to shoot. Right nimbly should we leap, proud and high, If the King's Son should be with Cathleen Ni Houlihan!

3. Long are we watching still for our deliverance, Rustics as we are, without raiment or its where-

withal in our hands. Ships full laden will be riding the waves and the sea will re-echo When the King's Son comes to Cathleen Ni Houlihan!

4. Let not the wretches imagine that our agony will last for ever, Bonds burst soonest when the case is hardest. Moses made a strand of the great sea before the people of Israel, And may Christ have compassion on thee, Cathleen Ni Houlihan!

The author of this song is Liam Ó hIfearnáin (William Heffernan), who was born about 1720 at Lattin, about a mile and a half from Shronell, in the south of County Tipperary, and died there in 1803. Tradition says that the poet was blind from birth and he is commonly known as Liam Dall (Blind William).

The tune most usually associated with the song is that noted by Bunting in 1806 from Charles Byrne, the harper, and published by him in his 1840 volume with the title of "Kitty Nowlan". But I agree with Petrie's view that this is an instrumental tune—at any rate in the settings given by Bunting and others. The melody which I unite here for the first time to the words is from a manuscript of Bunting's, where it is entitled "Kathleen Nowlan". This name, like "Kitty Nowlan", may be taken to be a mistranslation of "Caitilín Ní Uallacháin". It is clearly a song air, and it is admirably suited to Heffernan's words. A version, called "The Tailor's Son", was noted from oral tradition by Lady Ferguson, and the well-known song "The Lark in the Clear Air" was written to it by her husband Sir Samuel Ferguson, the poet.

The reference to Spain in the first line of our song offers us a clue to its date. Except for a brief space, that country was at peace for the whole of Heffernan's adult life. In 1775 war broke out between England and the American Colonies; the following year, after Burgoyne's surrender, France came in on the side of the Colonists (Rodney's victory over the French, mentioned in the note to the previous song, belongs to this period); and in 1779 Spain also declared war, to be followed almost immediately by Holland. It might well have seemed to the blind poet in Tipperary that England's hour had struck. The Spanish effort was wholly concentrated on the siege and blockade of Gibraltar—the longest and most memorable to which the Rock has ever been subjected; and the attack was not finally and completely repulsed till July, 1782.

We may therefore, with some probability, assign Heffernan's poem to the period 1779–1782. The point is of some interest because this is the only poem in which the name "Caitilín Ní Uallacháin" is used as a synonym for Ireland; so that, if our surmise be correct, this identification (now so familiar) did not occur until towards the close of the eighteenth century. It may seem odd that, at so late a date, an Irish poet should envisage the possibility of the return of the Stuarts; but nearly all these men wrote in a conventional style which had small regard to contemporary realities. Only one of them—the Clare poet Tomás Ó Míocháin (Meehan)—wrote songs on the American War of Independence and the Irish Volunteer Movement of 1782.

There is not much doubt that the original Caitilín Ní Uallacháin was the heroine of a (non-extant) love song, written in the same metre and sung to the same tune, to which she gave her name. That name, when used in English, should be Cathleen Houlihan or O' Houlihan or (if it is desired to retain the Ní, which is the feminine of Ó) Cathleen Ní Oulihan, since the initial H is dropped in the feminine. But the H has been sanctified by romantic usage, on which ground (and the ground of euphony) I have retained it in my translation. It remains to add that the song was translated into English verse by Mangan; but he misconstrues the Irish in places and his version, not being in the strict metre of the original, cannot be sung to the tune.

DRUIMFHIONN DONN DÍLIS   DRIMIN DHOWN DEELISH

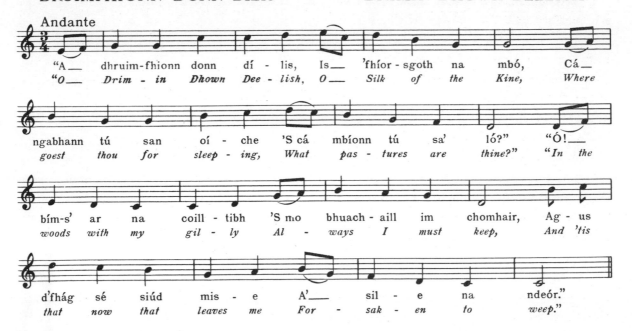

Andante

"A dhruim-fhionn donn dí - lis, Is_ 'fhíor - sgoth na mbó, Cá_
"O_ Drim - in Dhown Dee - lish, O_ Silk of the Kine, Where

ngabhann tú san oí - che 'S cá mbíonn tú sa' ló?" "Ó!_
goest thou for sleep - ing, What pas - tures are thine?" "In the

bím-s' ar na coill - tibh 'S mo bhuach - aill im chomhair, Ag - us
woods with my gil - ly Al - ways I must keep, And 'tis

d'fhág sé siúd mis - e A'_ sil - e na ndeór."
that now that leaves me For - sak - en to weep."

"A dhruimfhionn donn dílis
  Is 'fhíor-sgoth na mbó,
Cá ngabhann tú san oíche,
  'S cá mbíonn tú sa' ló?"
"Ó! hím-se ar na coilltibh
  'S mo bhuachaill im chomhair,
Agus d'fhág sé siúd mise
  A' síle na ndeór.

"Níl fearann, níl tíos agam,
  Níl fíonta ná ceól,
Níl flaithibh am choimhdeacht,
  Níl saoithe ná slógh:
Ach a' síor-ól an uisge
  Go minic sa' ló,
Agus beathuisge 's fíon
  Ag mo naimhdibh ar bórd."

"Dá bhfaighinn-se cead aighnis,
  Nó radharc ar a' gcoróinn,
Sasanaigh do leidhbfinn
  Mar do leidhbfinn seana-bhróg,
Trí bhogaithe, trí choillte,
  Is trí dhraighneach lá ceó—
Agus siúd mar do sheólfainn
  Mo dhruimfhionn donn óg!"

"O Drimin Dhown Deelish!
  O Silk of the Kine!
Where goest thou for sleeping?
  What pastures are thine?"
"In the woods with my gilly
  Always I must keep,
And 'tis that now that leaves me
  Forsaken to weep.

"Land, homestead, wines, music,
  I am reft of them all!
Chief and bard that once wooed me
  Are gone from my call!
And cold water to soothe me
  I sup with my tears,
While the foe that pursues me
  Has the drinking that cheers."

"Through the mist of the glensides
  And hills I'll return:
Like a brogue beyond mending
  The Sasanach I'll spurn:
If in battle's contention
  I have sight of the crown,
I'll befriend thee and defend thee,
  My young Drimin Dhown!"

THOMAS MACDONAGH

1. "O beloved brown Drimin, True flower of the kine, Whither do you fare at night, And where do you keep in the day?" "O! I keep on the hills, With my herdsman tending me, And it is this that has left me Shedding tears.

2. "I have no land, no homestead, Neither wines nor music, There are no princes in attendance on me, No nobles nor hosts. But I drink nothing but water Oft-times in the day, While there is whiskey and wine On the table of my enemies."

3. "If I could get leave to plead, Or a glimpse of the crown, I would tear up the English As I would tear up an old shoe, Through bogs, through hills, And through thorny places on a day of mist, And that is how I would herd My young brown Drimin!"

The manner in which folk songs and airs were turned by the poets to patriotic uses has already been dealt with in the Introduction to this section. Most of these were love songs, in which the name of the girl who gave the song its title is transferred to Ireland; but in this case the choice falls—rather incongruously, as we may think—on a favourite cow. The result, nevertheless, is of a stark and melancholy beauty which well suggests the miseries of the Penal Days. The title means literally "Beloved brown white-backed [cow]".

Tunes with this or a similar title are not rare in Irish musical manuscripts and printed books; and in the Bunting papers there is a set of words on the death of a pet cow, entitled "Druimin Dubh Ó!" This will go to the tune printed at p. 32 of his 1840 volume, where he gives the chorus in phonetic spelling and a prose translation of the verses. Songs with the same title and theme are also known in Scotland. There is a reference to one of them in Scott's *Waverley*, and Burns wrote his song for Mrs. McLachlan ("Musing on the roaring ocean") to a Highland air called "Druimin Dubh."

HISTORICAL SONGS

The historical songs of the Irish are for the most part episodic. They do not treat of great events in a general way, but rather with the results of those events as personally seen and experienced by individuals, known or unknown. Hence they require for their proper understanding a fairly full annotation, and this I have tried to provide in the case of the five songs which follow. They range from the Cromwellian Settlement of 1652 to the anti-tithe agitation of the early nineteenth century.

SEÁN Ó DUÍR A' GHLEANNA   JOHN O'DWYER OF THE GLEN

Ar m'éirghe dhom ar maidin,
Grian a' tsamhraidh 'taitneamh,
Chuala 'n uaill dá casa,
    'Gus ceól binn na n-éan;
Bruic is míolta gearra,
Creabhair na ngob fada,
Sound ag a' macalla,
    'Gus lamhach gunnaí tréan:
An sionnach rua ar a' gcarraig,
Míle liú ag marcaigh,
Is bean go dúch sa' mbealach
    Ag áireamh a gé.
Anois tá'n choill dá gearra,
Triallfaimíd thar cala,
'S a Sheáin Uí Dhuír a' Ghleanna,
    Chaill tú do chéim!

Oft at pleasant morning,
Sunshine all adorning,
I've heard the horn give warning,
    With birds' mellow call:
Badgers flee before us,
Woodcocks startle o'er us,
Guns make ringing chorus
    Mid the echoes all;
The fox run high and higher,
Horsemen shouting nigher,
The maiden mourning by her
    Fowl he left in gore.
Now, they fell the wild-wood,
Farewell, home of childhood,
Ah, Shaun O'Dwyer a Glanna,
    Thy day is o'er!

147

Is é sin m'uaigneas fada,
Sgáth mo chluas dá ghearra,
An ghaoth adtuaidh am leatha,
    Agus bás ins an spéir;
Mo ghadhairín suairc dá cheangal
Gan chead lúith ná aisdíocht,
Do bhainfeadh gruaim den leanbh
    I meán ghil an lae.
'Sé rí na h-uaisle 'r an gcarraig
An ceáfrach buacach, beannach,
Do thiocfadh suas ar aiteann
    Go lá dheire 'n tsaéil;
'S dá bhfaghainn-se suaineas tamall
Ó dhaoinibh uaisle 'n bhaile,
Do thriallfainn féin ar Ghaillimh,
    Agus d'fhágfainn an sgléip.

Táid fearainn ghleanna 'n tsrotha
Gan cheann ná teann ar lochtaibh,
I sráid na gcuach ní molfar
    A sláinte ná a saol;
Mo loma luain gan fosga
Ó Chluain go Stuaic na gcolum,
'S an gearrfhia ar bruach an Rosa
    Ar fán le n-a ré.
Créad í an ruaig so ar thoraibh,
Buala buan a mbona?
An smóilín binn 's an londubh
    Gan sár-ghuth ar ghéig;
'S gur mór an tuar chun cogaidh
Cléir go buartha 's pobail,
Dá seóla 'gcuantaibh loma
    I lár ghleanna 'n tslé.

Is é mo chreach ar maidin
Nach bhfuair mé bás gan pheaca
Sar a bhfuair mé sgannall
    Fá mo chuid féin—
'S a liacht lá breá fada
Thig úla cumhra 'r chrannaibh,
Duilliúr ar an dair
    Agus drúcht ar an bhféar.
'Nois táim-se ruaigthe óm fhearann,
I n-uaigneas 'bhfad óm charaid,
Im luí go duairc faoi sgairtibh,
    'S i gcuasaibh an tslé;
'S muna bhfagha mé suaineas feasta
Ó dhaoinibh uaisle 'n bhaile,
Tréigfidh mé mo shealbh
    Agus fágfad an saol.

It is my sorrow sorest,
Woe—the falling forest!
The north wind gives me no rest,
    And death's in the sky:
My faithful hound's tied tightly,
Never sporting brightly,
Who'd make a child laugh lightly,
    With tears in his eye.
The antlered, noble-hearted
Stags are never started,
Never chased nor parted
    From the furzy hills.
If peace came, but a small way,
I'd journey down on Galway,
And leave, though not for alway,
    My Erin of ills.

The land of streamy valleys
Hath no head nor rallies,
In city, camp or palace
    They never toast her name.
Alas, no warrior column
From Cloyne to peaks of Colum,
O'er wasted fields and solemn
    The shy hares grow tame.
Oh, when shall come the routing,
The flight of churls and flouting?
We hear no joyous shouting
    From the blackbird brave:
More warlike is the omen,
Justice comes to no men,
Priests must flee the foemen
    To the mountain cave.

It is my woe and ruin
That sinless death's undoing
Came not ere the strewing
    Of all my bright hopes.
How oft, at sunny morning,
I've watched the spring returning,
The autumn apples burning,
    And dew on woodland slopes!
Now my lands are plunder,
Far my friends asunder,
I must hide me under
    Branch and bramble screen;
If soon I cannot save me
By flight from foes who crave me,
O Death, at last I'll brave thee
    My bitter foes between!

GEORGE SIGERSON

1. When I rose in the morning, And the summer sun was shining, I heard the [huntsman's] cry being raised, And the sweet song of birds; I heard badgers and hares, The long-billed woodcocks, The sound of the echo, And the shots of loud guns: The red fox on the rock, The horsemen hallooing, And a woman by the roadside sadly Counting her geese. But now the wood is being cut down, We shall go across the seas, Oh, John O'Dwyer of the Glen, You have lost your lordship!

2. This is my abiding grief, The shelter of my head that is being cut down, The north wind knocks me over, And death is in the sky; My merry little dog is chained up, He cannot frolic or exercise, Who would delight the children In the middle of the brightness of the day. The noblest of all on the rock Is the bounding, proud, antlered [stag], Who would live on furze Till the last day of the world. And if I could get some respite From the gentlefolks here, I would make my way to Galway And leave sport behind.

3. The pleasant riverside country Has now no chief or ruler for its peoples, In the village where the goblets are Their health and long life will no longer be proposed. Alas! there is now no shelter From Clonmel(?) to pigeon-haunted Stuaic (? Stook, in north Tipperary), The hare wanders all his life On the threshold of Ross. What is [the meaning of] this attack on bushes, This constant striking at their roots? No more will the song thrush and the blackbird Whistle on the bough; And 'tis a sad presage of war When the harassed clergy and congregations Are driven out to shelterless resorts In the deep valleys and mountains.

4. Woe is me That I did not die a sinless death Before I earned opprobrium Over what is my own! —Seeing that on so many a fine long day Scented apples come on the trees, Foliage on the oak And dew on the grass. Now I am driven from my lands, In solitude afar from my friends, Sadly lurking beneath bushes And in mountain recesses; And if I get not peace henceforth From the gentlefolks here, I shall abandon my patrimony And quit this life.

But for what has happened and is happening in Europe in our own day, one would say that the Cromwellian "settlement" of Ireland was the worst example of spoliation in modern history. Six of the Ulster counties had already been planted by James I some half century earlier; and now, immediately after the conclusion of the war in 1652, Leinster, Munster and the three remaining counties of Ulster were similarly dealt with. Ten counties were divided between the English soldiers and the greedy Adventurers of 1642, who had furnished the Long Parliament with money for its army in Ireland; and the remainder went to satisfy the arrears of pay of the mercenaries and the liabilities incurred in the campaign. The "mere Irish" were forcibly transported to the barren lands of Connacht, with every circumstance of cruelty. Thousands, indeed, were despatched further afield, being sent into virtual slavery in the Barbados.

In this song the pleasant, carefree life of a country gentleman in Tipperary before hostilities is set in vivid contrast to the desolation and ruin imposed by Cromwell, and the horror and cold inhumanity of the "settlement" are brought out by a witness and a victim— but rather by allusion and reminiscence than by direct statement. People and clergy forced to seek a refuge in the fastnesses of the hills; the landowning aristocracy uprooted from the territories that had been theirs for centuries; the landscape desecrated by the razing of the forests—a measure doubtless taken to forestall guerrilla warfare; the sad necessity of abandoning home and country to seek service in the armies of France or Austria or Spain.

In the Introduction to the Patriotic Songs I have mentioned that Dr. Sigerson's stressing of the patriotic note in verse 3 of his translation is not justified by the text. There are two other places in which he appears to have missed the point. In verse 2, the suggestion is that the stag is now the only noble left; and in verse 4 the poet compares his own condition to that of inanimate nature: apples are on the trees, foliage on the oak, dew on the grass. He alone fails to receive that which is his own.

John O'Dwyer of the Glen was the third son of Darby O'Dwyer (died 1629), who was Chief of the O'Dwyers of Kilnamanagh and lived at Cloniharp Castle, now a ruin, near Dundrum, County Tipperary. The glen from which John O'Dwyer took his epithet "*an ghleanna*" is a matter of uncertainty, and it has been variously supposed to be the Glen of Aherlow at the base of the Galtee Mountains, Glenough, in the parish of Clonoulty, and Glenefy near Galbally. We know little of his history, but it may be fairly assumed that during the war of 1649–1652 he was closely associated with his cousin Colonel Edmund O'Dwyer. It is clear from the second verse that he foresaw that he would be compelled to leave Ireland, and it is probable that he accompanied his cousin into exile.

Colonel Edmund O'Dwyer had operated in Tipperary, Waterford and Limerick, commanding a brigade of five regiments against the Cromwellian forces. The city of Limerick having fallen in October, 1651, the Irish cause was rendered hopeless; and so, by the Treaty of Cahir, 23rd March, 1652, O'Dwyer surrendered on terms. He was allowed to proceed with 4,500 of his officers and men to join the Spanish army commanded by the Prince of Condé in Flanders, which was then fighting the French under Turenne. The party sailed from Cove, and Colonel Edmund O'Dwyer was killed while leading his troops against Arras in August, 1654.

149

"Cé h-é sin amuh
Go bhfuil faor ar a ghuth,
  A' réaba mo dhoruis dúnta?"
"Mise Éamonn a' Chnuic,
Tá báidhte fuar fliuch
  Ó shíor-shiúl sléibhte is gleannta."
"A lao ghil 's a chuid,
Cad do dhéanfainn-se dhuit
  Mara gcuirfinn ort beinn dom ghúna?
'S go mbeidh púdar dubh
'Á lamhach linn go tiubh,
  Is go mbeimís araon múchta!"

"Is fada mise amuh
Faoi shneachta is faoi shioc,
  Is gan dánacht agam ar éinne,
Mo bhranar gan cur,
Mo sheisreach gan sgur,
  Is gan iad agam ar aon chor!
Níl caraid agam
(Is danaid liom san)
  Do ghlacfadh mé moch ná déanach,
Is go gcaithfe mé dul
Thar fairrge soir,
  Ó's ann ná fuil mo ghaolta!"

"O who is without
That with passionate shout
  Keeps beating my bolted door?"
"I am Ned of the Hill,
Forspent wet and chill
  From long trudging marsh and moor."
"My love fond and true,
What else could I do
  But shield you from wind and from weather?
When the shots fall like hail
They us both shall assail,
  And mayhap we shall die together!"

"Through frost and through snow
Tired and hunted I go,
  In fear both from friend and from neighbour,
My horses run wild,
My acres untilled,
  And they all of them lost to my labour.
But it grieves me far more
Than the loss of my store
  That there's none who would shield me from danger;
So my fate it must be
To fare eastward o'er sea,
  And languish amid the stranger!"

DONAL O'SULLIVAN

1. " Who is that without, With passion in his voice, That beats at my bolted door? " " I am Edmund of the Hill, Drenched, numbed and wet From long walking mountains and valleys." " My dearest, my treasure, What should I do for you But cover you with the skirt of my dress? For black gunpowder Will be thickly shot at us, And we should perish together! "

2. " Long am I abroad In snow and in frost, Not daring to approach any man, My fallow unsown, My horses unloosened, And they lost to me entirely! Friends I have none (I grieve for that) Who would harbour me early or late, And so I must go Eastward over the sea, For it is there I have no kindred! "

Fifty years after John O'Dwyer of the Glen comes Edmund Ryan of the Hill, from the same district of the same county of Tipperary and, on his mother's side, of the same family—for she was one of the O'Dwyers of Kilnamanagh; and the Ryans, like the O'Dwyers, were wealthy landowners whose estates had been seized by the Cromwellians. Broken under Cromwell, the Irish made one last despairing bid for independence, led by Sarsfield against the forces of William of Orange; but they suffered irretrievable defeat at the Boyne and at Aughrim, and under the terms of the Capitulation of Limerick (3rd October, 1691) most of Ireland's fighting men, called "the Wild Geese", left for the Continent, there to continue the struggle in the Irish Brigades on many a battlefield "from Dunkirk to Belgrade".

Most, but by no means all. Some of the most gallant and intrepid remained at home to carry on an independent fight by every means in their power: constantly raiding the encampments of the English soldiery, harassing its lines of communication, and retreating to their hide-outs in the hills, each man of them with a price on his head. They were known as rapparees (Irish *ropairí*)—what we should nowadays call an underground movement; and one of the most heroic of them all was Edmund Ryan of the Hill.

He was born at Knockmeoll Castle (Irish *Cnoc Maothail*) on the hill of that name, 828 feet high, in the parish of Templebeg; and for that reason he is always known as *Éamonn an Chnuic*—Edmund of the Hill. I have published elsewhere, from manuscripts and oral tradition, all that is now likely to be discoverable of this remarkable man, whose gay chivalry, daring exploits and "moving accidents by flood and field" would indeed make fine material for an historical novel. Precise dates are for the most part lacking; but there existed in the former Irish Record Office (destroyed with all its contents in the Civil War of 1922) a Government Proclamation, dated 1702, offering a reward of £200 for the apprehension of "Edmund Knock Ryan". His outlawry is undoubted, for in one version of the song the hero announces himself thus:

> 'Sé Eamonn an Chnuic atá agat ann,
> 'S is daor anois in a dhúthaigh!

> ('Tis Ned of the Hill that you have here,
> And proscribed is he now in his country!)

Some verses are of a strange, erotic beauty, which shows Ryan to have been at once a passionate lover and an accomplished poet; but the two that I give here are outstanding. The first, with a striking economy of language, conjures up an unforgettable picture of the lonely outlaw seeking shelter and of the girl who offers to protect him against the bullets of his enemies, if need be with her own body; and in the second we are given a vivid description of the poet's temporal ruin, his present hunted state and his intention to make his way east to Europe, even as the Wild Geese had done a few years earlier.

Unfortunately, this intention was frustrated. While Ryan was asleep in the house of a man named Dwyer, the latter killed him with a hatchet for the purpose of obtaining the reward on his head. The miscreant was unaware, however, of what had happened a few days previously. A common robber had stolen £80 from one of the English, Maude of

Dundrum. Ryan, hearing of this, borrowed the best horse in Maude's stable, tracked down the thief and chivalrously restored the money. In gratitude for this deed, Maude successfully exerted himself to get the proscription removed. Hence Ryan's murderer arrived at Cashel with the severed head of his victim only to find that he had had his trouble for nothing. And so the story ends with an unexpectedness and irony reminiscent of a tale by Hardy or Maupassant.

PRÍOSÚN CHLUAIN MEALA   THE GAOL OF CLONMEL

Ó! bliain is lá amáireach
  'Sea d'fhágas an baile
A' dul go h-Árd Pádraig,
  'Cur lásaí lem hata.
Bhí Buachaillí Bána ann,
  Is rás aca ar Eallaibh,
Is mé go dúch uaigneach
  I bpríosún Chluain Meala.

Tá mo shrian agus m'iallait
  Ar iasacht le fada,
Mo chamán ar fiara
  Fé iarthar mo leapa,
Mo liathróid dá buala
  Ag buachaillí an ghleanna—
Is go mbuailfinn poc báire
  Chomh h-árd leis na fearaibh!

A Chiarraígh, bídh a' guí liom,
  Is bog binn liom bhur nglórtha,
Is beag a shaoileas-sa choíche
  Ná fillfinn-se beó orraibh:
Go mbeidh ár dtrí cinn-ne
  Ar trí spící mar sheó aca,
Fé shneachta na h-oíche
  Is gach síon eile 'á ngeóidh chúinn!

How hard is my fortune,
  And vain my repining!
The strong rope of fate
  For this young neck is twining.
My strength is departed,
  My cheek sunk and sallow,
While I languish in chains
  In the gaol of Cluain Meala.

No boy in the village
  Was ever yet milder,
I'd play with a child
  And my sport would be wilder.
I'd dance without tiring
  From morning till even,
And the goal-ball I'd strike
  To the lightning of heaven!

At my bed-foot decaying
  My hurl-bat is lying,
Through the boys of the village
  My goal-ball is flying.
My horse 'mongst the neighbours
  Neglected may fallow,
While I pine in my chains
  In the gaol of Cluain Meala.

Go h-Uíbh Ráthach má théann tú,
  Beir sgéal go dtí mo mhuinntir,
Go bhfuilim daor ar an bhfód so,
  Is ná fuil beó agam ach go h-Aoine.
Bailídh gléas tórraimh
  Agus comhra bhreá im thímpal,
Sin críoch ar Ó Domhnaill,
  Is go deó bídh a' guí leis!

Next Sunday the patron
  At home will be keeping,
And the young active hurlers
  The field will be sweeping.
With the dance of fair maidens
  The evening they'll hallow,
While this heart, once so gay,
  Shall be cold in Cluain Meala.

J. J. CALLANAN

1. It will be a year to-morrow Since I left home, To go to Ardpatrick, Putting lace in my hat. Whiteboys were there, Racing at Duhallow(?), While I lie sad and lonely In the gaol of Clonmel.

2. My bridle and saddle Are lent out this long time, My hurley is warping Behind my bed, My ball is being struck By the lads of the valley—And I would hit a goaling-stroke As high as the men!

3. Kerrymen, pray for me, I love your soft musical voices, 'Tis little I ever thought That I should not return to you alive: Or that our three heads Would be exhibited by them on three spikes, In the snow of the night-time, And any other weather that might come!

4. If you go to Iveragh, Take the news to my people, That I am condemned on this spot, And have only till Friday to live. Get together material for the wake, And a fine coffin for me, That is the end of O'Donnell, And pray for him always!

From about the middle of the second half of the eighteenth century the evils of land-lordism—usually absentee landlordism—were at their height. In Ulster, the people had to complain of excessive rents and excessive tithes, and they were compelled to build roads to the cost of which the landlords contributed nothing. In Munster, common lands used for grazing and turbary were enclosed; farms were consolidated and the smaller tenants set adrift; rack rents were universal. This condition of affairs gave rise to secret, oath-bound societies. The Ulstermen formed the Oakboys, who wore sprigs of oak in their hats; and the Munstermen formed the *Buachaillí Bána* or Whiteboys, so called because they wore shirts over their clothes—partly for disguise and partly for mutual identification at night, when they chiefly operated.

Undoubtedly, the Whiteboys were guilty of grave excesses, such as burning home-steads, houghing cattle and inflicting on their victims the inhuman punishment known as "carding", that is to say, scraping the naked back with a steel wool-card. But these excesses were perhaps a measure of their grievances, and it must be remembered that no constitutional redress was possible to people who, because of their religion, were denied the parliamentary franchise and debarred from election to any public body. The support of the masses was solidly behind the movement, as a contemporary ballad in English shows:

Success to the Whiteboys—we've a few of them here,
We'll toast their good health in both whiskey and beer;
And long may they reign over country and town,
For they are the boys that keep land-jobbers down!

Of the hapless youth who is the subject of the present song we know nothing except what we are told by the song itself; but it is clear from the first verse (Irish version) that it dates from the period we have been discussing. The Whiteboys were his companions, and presumably he was one of them. His name was O'Donnell, he came from Iveragh, County Kerry, and he was to be hanged in Clonmel Gaol on the following Friday—apparently with two fellow-victims. Their heads would be severed from their bodies and exhibited on spikes at the gate of the prison, as a warning to others and in accordance with the barbarous custom of the time.

EOGHAN CÓIR

OWEN CÓIR

Joviale

Nach é seo an sgéal deac-rach sa' tír seo,__ I-
Is-n't this the most pit-i-ful stor - y__ That__

n-an-ac-air chroí 'gus__ brón,__ Ó__ fhág-as tú Creag-án a' Lín - e__ Go
ev - er touched heart to the core?__ To - day we saw Ow-en to glor - y__ From

dté tú go dti'n Fál Mór?__ A lei-thead de sgread-a 's de
Creag - an - a - line to Fall - more.__ Such wail-ing and loud lam-ent-

chaoin - e Níor chual-aidh tú 'riamh go__ fóill,__ Cidh
-a - tion Were ne'er heard in Er - in__ be - fore,__ For we've

níl__ a-gainn-ne aon iongn-a__ Ó__ caill-eadh, fá-ríor! Eoghan Cóir!__
lost our best friend in cre - a - tion,__ The kind, ten-der-heart-ed Ow-en Cóir!__

Nach é seo an sgéal deacrach san tír seo,
    I n-anacair chroí 'gus brón,
Ó fhágas tú Creagán an Líne
    Go dté tú go dtí an Fál Mór?
A leithead de sgreada 's de chaoine
    Níor chualaidh tú ariamh go fóill,
Cidh níl againn-ne aon iongna,
    Ó cailleadh, fá-ríor! Eoghan Cóir!

Bhí grá agus gean ag gach n-aon air,
    An seanduine críon 's an t-óg,
Bhí an saidhbhir 's an daidhbhir i ngnaoi leis
    Mar gheall ar a chroí maith mór
Le togha 'gus le rogha na tíre
    Do chaitheadh sé píosaí óir.
'S le daoine bocht' eile níor spíd leis
    Buidéal den tsíbín d'ól.

Tá Antoine Ó Gabháin a' caoine,
    'S ní bheidh Seán Ó Baoghail i bhfad beó,
Ó cailleadh a gcaraid san tír seo,
    'Sé d'fhágaibh a gcroí faoi bhrón.
I n-anacair chathair níor síneadh,
    'Sé mheasaim, fá líag ná fód
Aoinneach ba mheasa don dís-se
    Ná an duine bocht maol, Eoghan Cóir!

Ba ró-mhaith a' tógbháil an chíosa é,
    Ba bheag aige mí nó dhó,
Go ndíoltaí an bhó ar an aonach,
    Nó an giota do bhíodh san tseól.
'Sé dúirt Séamus Pheadair Mhic Riabhaigh,
    Is é ag agairt ar Rí na ndeór,
" Do réir mar bhí seisean do dhaoinibh,
    Gurab amhlaidh bheas Críosta dhó! "

Isn't this the most pitiful story
    That ever touched heart to the core?
To-day we saw Owen to glory
    From Creagan-a-line to Fallmore.
Such wailing and loud lamentation
    Were ne'er heard in Erin before,
For we've lost our best friend in creation,
    The kind, tender-hearted Owen Cóir!

He had everyone's love and affection,
    The withered old man and the young;
With the highest and lowest connection
    The praise of his big heart was sung.
With the pick and the pride of the people
    Although he liked best to spend free,
He'd never say " No! " to a tipple
    From folks of the poorest degree.

Poor Gavin's in deep tribulation,
    And Boyle won't be long to the fore,
Since they lost their best friend in creation
    Their hearts are with grief brimming o'er.
There never, I'm thinking, yet measured
    His length in the battle's uproar
A hero this couple more cherished
    Than the soft-hearted " craythur ", Owen Cóir.

'Twas he that was good at rent-taking,
    Made light of a month here and there,
Till you'd sell the frieze cloth you'd be making,
    Or your young heifer calf at the fair.
'Twas thinking of all his good labours
    Made Shamus so fervently pray,
" The same as he was to the neighbours
    May Jesus be to him this day! "

155

Aon agus seacht ins a' líne,
  Agus ocht do chur síos faoi dhó,
Tráth ghlac seisean cead le n-a dhaoine
  'S níor labhair sé gíog níos mó.
Tá sé dearbhtha, sgríobhtha
  Gur talamh is críoch do ghach beó,
Is chomh fhad is bheimíd san tsaol so
  Cá mhisde dhúinn braon beag d'ól?

                RIOCARD BAIRÉAD

Put one in a line with a seven,
  And eight after that doubled o'er,*
He went on his journey to—heaven,
  And the devil a word he spoke more.
'Tis laid down by poet and prophet
  Some day to the grave we'll all go,
But while we can keep our legs off it,
  A drink is the best cure for woe!

                FRANCIS A. FAHY

*1788

1. Is not this a painful event in the countryside, [With everyone] in distress of mind and sorrow From where you leave Creagan-a-line Till you get to Fallmore? Such crying and lamentation You never heard yet, Although it is no wonder for us, Since, alas! Owen Cóir has died!

2. He had everyone's love and affection, The withered old man and the young, Rich and poor doted on him, Because of his great, good heart. With the choicest and best in the land He would spend gold pieces, And with the others, the poor people, he would make no bones About drinking a bottle of beer.

3. Anthony Gavin is lamenting, And John Boyle will not live for long; Since they lost their best friend in the countryside Their hearts have been sorrowful. Amid a [whole] city's grief there never was laid to rest, In my opinion, under tombstone or sod, Anyone who was dearer to these two Than the poor, simple man, Owen Cóir.

4. He was very good at rent-collecting, He did not worry about a month or two, Till the cow would be sold at the fair, Or the bit of cloth that was in the loom. Said James, son of Peter MacGreevy, Praying to the King of tears, " According as he treated the people, May Christ treat him the same ! "

5. One and seven in a line, Followed by a double eight, Was when he took leave of his people, And he never uttered another sound. It is truly written That the earth is the end of all living, And so long as we are alive What harm for us to take a drop of drink?

In the notes to the previous song mention has been made of the exactions suffered by the farmers of Ulster and Munster at the hands of the landlords. The position in the province of Connacht was even worse. The land was poorer, absenteeism was greater, and the management of estates was largely in the hands of the land-agents—a class of men notorious for their rapacity and inhumanity.

One such was Eoghan Ó Conmacháin (the name would be rendered "Owen Conway" in English), agent to the Binghams in Erris, County Mayo, who was nicknamed "Eoghan Cóir", meaning, ironically, "Honest Owen". (The adjective *cóir*, pronounced *core*, connotes civility, decency, fair play.) He died in 1788 and is buried in the graveyard of Tearmon Caithreach (Termoncarragh), about four miles north-west of Belmullet.

The poet Richard Barrett of Erris was his contemporary and neighbour, and the delightful satire of his "elegy" on the land-agent calls for no comment or gloss. The prayer—or imprecation—in the fourth verse recalls Villon's wish for the Bishop of Orleans, who had had him dropped into a pit in the Tour de Manasses in the gaol of Meung:

    Vecy tout le mal que j'en dis:
    S'il m'a esté misericors,
    Jhesus, le roy de Paradis,
    Tel luy soit à l'âme et au corps!

Another lively piece of Barrett's is included among the Drinking Songs (p. 117).

RÁISEANNA BHAILE ÁTHA ÚLA — THE RACES OF BALLYHOOLY

Tá sgéal ag-am le h-inn-sint is ná smaoin-idh gur bréag é, Cé gur
A sto-ry I've to tell you, friends, and 'tis no false re-la-tion, 'Tis

fad-a táim-íd síos aig-e síol rach na méir-leach, Beidh
all a-bout the thieving fiends that long op-pressed this na-tion. The

próc-ad-óir-í Galld-a go fann-lag gan éif-eacht, Gan
proc-tors and their her-es-ies will short-ly be sent pack-ing, Their

chlú, gan mheas, gan séan, gan rath, gan bia, gan deoch, gan éad-ach.
creed and doc-trines all proved lies, their wines and vic-tuals lack-ing.

Preab-aidh in bhur seas-amh is árd-uídh bhur n-inn-tinn, Tá'n
For my news is this great mat-ter, boys, for which your hearts are yearn-ing, The

deach-ú leis a' bhfán is gan fáil chas-ta choích' air,
tithes we soon will scat-ter with-out hope of their re-turn-ing, The

Ruaig-fim-íd na h-Or-ange-men 'gus déan-faim-íd a ndíb-irt; Beidh
O-range-men we'll bat-ter, all their pleas for mer-cy spurn-ing; The

min-is-trí fé bhrón is a ndóir-se 'ca dún-ta, 'S ba
min-is-ters will lose what's theirs, their doors shut in their fac-es, Be

bhinn-e leat an lá úd ná Ráis-eann-a Bh'l'Áth' Úl-a!
sure that day will be far more gay than the Bal-ly-hoo-ly Rac-es!

157

Tá sgéal agam le h-innsint
    is ná smaoinidh gur bréag é,
Cé gur fada táimíd síos
    aige síolrach na méirleach,
Beidh prócadóirí Gallda
    go fann-lag gan éifeacht,
Gan chlú, gan mheas, gan séan, gan rath
    gan bia, gan deoch, gan éadach.
Preabaidh in bhur seasamh
    is árduídh bhur n-inntinn,
Tá an deachú leis a' bhfán
    is gan fáil chasta choíche air,
Ruaigfimíd na h-*Orangemen*
    'gus déanfaimíd a ndíbirt;
Beidh ministrí fé bhrón
    is a ndóirse aca dúnta—
'S ba bhinne leat an lá úd
    ná Ráiseanna Bh'l' Áth' Úla!

A story I've to tell you, friends,
    and 'tis no false relation,
'Tis all about the thieving fiends
    that long oppressed this nation.
The proctors and their heresies
    will shortly be sent packing,
Their creed and doctrines all proved lies,
    their wines and victuals lacking.
For my news is this great matter, boys,
    for which your hearts are yearning,
The tithes we soon will scatter,
    without hope of their returning,
The Orangemen we'll batter,
    all their pleas for mercy spurning.
The ministers will lose what's theirs,
    their doors shut in their faces,
Be sure that day will be far more gay
    than the Ballyhooly races!

Ar an nGort Rua do thuit ár gcómharsain
    le h-órduithe láimhte,
Beidh Ríocht gheal na Glóire
    go deó aca mar árus;
Beidh Dia mór na gCómhacht ann
    i gcóir go bhfuíom sásamh,
Go gcrochtar iad le córda nó
    go ndóitear 'n-a gcnámhnaibh.
Má thigid na sméirligh saor
    abhaile ón gcúis seo,
Beifar 'n-a gcóir fós,
    mo bhrón-sa! Lá an Chúntais;
Beidh fuil na bhfíréan idir
    an spéir is a súile,
Beidh an dial is a ghárda
    dá n-árdach chun siúil leis—
'S ba bhinne leat an lá úd
    ná Ráiseanna Bh'l' Áth' Úla!

'Twas at Gortroe our neighbours died
    through shooting fell and gory,
The gates of heaven are opened wide
    to welcome them to glory.
Almighty God will not forget
    these men, for all their boasting,
On the gallows tree we'll see them yet,
    or in a furnace roasting.
If fire and gibbet they can cheat,
    for them there's no repentance,
They still must face the Judgement Seat
    and hear the dreadful sentence,
Our martyrs will their pleas defeat,
    they'll all of them be sent hence.
The devil then will seize these men
    and put them through their paces—
Be sure that day will be far more gay
    than the Ballyhooly Races!

Le trí chéad bliain d'fhág Séamus bréan
    ár n-aigne go buartha,
Fé bhrón, fé smacht, gan chóir, gan cheart,
    ach allus le n-ár ngruanaibh,
Ár n-Eaglais a' léamh Aifrinn
    le h-anaithe i ngleanntaibh,
'S a dtréada 'dul ar strae aca
    gach éan-mhaidin Domhnaigh.
Anois tá eagla ar chách gur
    ar lár do bheidh a dteampuill,
Tá prapaí fé sna fallaí aca
    le h-anaithe 's le sgannra.
Beidh gach cloch is reacht aca
    caite thar a chéile,
Beidh ministrí ar lár
    is a gcnámha briste brúite—
'S ba bhinne leat an lá úd
    ná Ráiseanna Bh'l' Áth' Úla!

Three centuries the foreign race
    has ground us 'neath the harrow;
The sweat aye running down our face
    in travail and in sorrow;
Our priests, proscribed, were forced to say
    their Mass in secret hollow,
Each Sunday and each holy-day,
    alas! where few could follow.
But the foreigners will tremble soon,
    their downfall is beginning,
They'll see their churches crumble soon,
    in spite of under-pinning,
Each stone of them will tumble soon,
    their steeples all sent spinning.
We'll finish with the ministers,
    of their work we'll leave no traces—
Be sure that day will be far more gay
    than the Ballyhooly Races!

DONAL O'SULLIVAN

1. I have a story to tell, and do not think it is a lie, That although we are long oppressed by the race of plunderers The foreign proctors will be forspent and powerless, Their standing and reputation gone, luckless and unfortunate, lacking food and drink and clothing. Spring to your feet and lift up your hearts, The tithes are overthrown without prospect of ever returning. We shall rout the Orangemen and achieve their expulsion, The ministers will be in tribulation, with their doors closed—And that day will be sweeter to you than the Races of Ballyhooly!

2. At Gortroe our neighbours fell by orders to shoot, The bright Kingdom of Glory will be their abode for ever. The great God Almighty will be there to grant us retribution, That they may be hanged by a rope or burnt to the bone. If the villains come unscathed from this ordeal, They will yet be dealt with, my grief! on the Day of Judgement, The blood of the faithful will be between heaven and their sight. The devil and his minions will carry them off with him—And that day will be sweeter to you than the Races of Ballyhooly!

3. For three hundred years dirty James (John Bull) left our minds troubled, Sorrowful and bullied, without justice or rights, but with sweat on our cheeks, Our clergy saying Mass affrighted in the valleys, And their flocks going astray from them on each Sunday morning. Now they are all in terror that their churches will be levelled, They have put props under the walls in their fear and alarm. Every single stone and ordinance of theirs shall be overturned, The ministers will be laid low, their bones bruised and broken— And that day will be sweeter to you than the Races of Ballyhooly!

This is an anti-tithe song, dating from the thirties of the last century. The compelling of Irish Catholics to pay tithes to a Church which they repudiated, and which was maintained in power and affluence by an alien Government, was a thing revolting to natural justice: but to enforce that payment at the rifle's mouth from people who were in dire want was, quite literally and in the biblical sense, a sin crying to heaven for vengeance—"grinding the faces of the poor". And yet that was precisely what some of the Protestant ministers did —but happily by no means all. In Skibbereen, for instance, the parson, though he knew that the stricken people were living on seaweed and nettles, insisted on his tithes with an escort of police and yeomanry. The Catholics resisted and thirty of them were shot dead.

Under the wise guidance of O'Connell, who took his seat in Parliament after the Catholic Emancipation Act of 1829, the collection of tithes was met with passive resistance everywhere, and when cattle, crops or furniture were seized by the proctors and offered at public auction nobody would buy. The agitation persisted in spite of the savage Coercion Act of 1833, which gave power to prohibit meetings, to put districts under martial law and to impose a curfew; and it ended successfully with the passage in 1838 of an Act abolishing the tithe rent-charge.

The affair at Gortroe, mentioned in the second verse of our song, occurred on the 18th December, 1834—a week before Christmas Day—and it is usually referred to as "the massacre of Rathcormac". Both places are near Fermoy, County Cork. On that day the Rev. Archdeacon William Ryder (popularly known as "Black Billy" and a wrong reverend if ever there was one) left Fermoy for the widow Ryan's cottage at Gortroe, to collect tithes to the amount of four pounds sixteen shillings. He walked at the head of a formidable array: two companies of foot, one of dragoons and a large body of police.

Arrived at the spot, they found a hundred and fifty unarmed people offering passive resistance. Some of these had placed carts across the laneway leading to the cottage, in order to block the passage of the soldiers. The Riot Act was read without any provocation being offered, and Ryder then ordered the cavalry to fire. They did so. The people who found themselves in the laneway and the small kitchen-garden had no chance of escaping, and nine of them were shot dead. The youngest victim was the widow's son, a lad of twenty. The soldiers then cleared the laneway, dragging the carts over the bodies of the dead and dying; and they seized four stacks of corn adjacent to the cottage in satisfaction of Ryder's demand for tithes.

These facts were given in sworn evidence before a partially packed jury at the coroner's inquest. As the jury failed to agree, Counsel for the magistrates expressed his willingness to accept the decision of the majority, and a verdict of "wilful murder" was then returned. Nevertheless, no action was taken against the murderers.

The title of the song is derived from the last line of each verse and requires some explanation. Ballyhooly, like Gortroe, is close to Fermoy. In the Royal Irish Academy there is an unpublished Jacobite poem by Henry MacAuliffe of Funcheon, written in the same metre, having the same title, and with a similar end-line (MS. 24 C 56, p. 525). The date of this poem is given in the manuscript as 1745, and it is there stated (p. 826) that MacAuliffe composed his song "in the tent at the races of Ballyhooly". Hence it would seem that for a century before our anti-tithe song was written the Races of Ballyhooly were a synonym for jollity and fun. The corrupted English form of this place-name is regrettably ugly. In its proper Irish dress it has a pleasant sound (Bla Hoola) and a picturesque meaning—"The Place of the Ford of the Apples".

"MARY, PITY WOMEN!"

The pitiful theme of girls led astray and betrayed, being unhappily a commonplace of rural life everywhere, is naturally represented in folk song. So far as Ireland is concerned, such songs are found more frequently in manuscripts than in printed books, for reasons that may be readily understood; but it would be wrong to conclude from this (as has sometimes been done) that the subject is avoided by the folk singers. Edward Walsh, writing in 1847, affirmed that "in these Irish songs are to be found none of the indelicate and even gross allusions which so greatly disgrace the lyrical efforts of the best poets of England in the last century. Not but what Irish rhymers have often composed in the censurable manner to which we have alluded; but these reprehensible lays are to be found only in manuscripts and are never sung by the people". Anyone who has noted Irish Gaelic folk songs from oral tradition must be aware that this statement is hardly borne out by experience.

Usually we do not know, and cannot even hazard a guess at, the circumstances in which a song of the kind that we are considering came to be composed. Still, there are two types discernible, of which examples are given here. For some decades subsequent to the battles of the Boyne and of Aughrim (1690–1691) hundreds of irregular Irish soldiers were abroad in the country—rapparees, as they were called—every one of whom was a nomadic outlaw with a price on his head. The circumstances of their lives were scarcely conducive to the observance of a strict moral code; and it is obvious from some verses of the song "Edmund of the Hill" (included in the Historical Section, p. 150) that no such strictness was in fact observed. I have omitted these verses (which I have published in full elsewhere) merely to heighten the dramatic effect of the two that I print.

Secondly, there are the songs made by forlorn girls whose love had been won by men above their station in life and whose natural innocence had been betrayed. In the passionate "Blackthorn Tree" (which will be found among the Love Songs, p. 49) the boast is made that the loved one's hands "are not blistered from the shovel nor swollen by the spade"; and in another, not given here, a former lover reproaches his sweetheart :

Chuaidh tú i gcóiste 'gus tú gan bróga,
Is bhí tú ag ól leis ó oi'dhe go lá.

("You rode in a coach, barefoot as you were, And you stayed drinking with him till dawn.") The number of such songs is greater in Connacht than in the other Irish-speaking districts: probably because the Irish were poorer in that province than elsewhere, and their supplanters wealthier and more dissolute. Certain it is that in many a quiet countryside the tragedy of Tess was re-enacted, where he was a rich man with time on his hands and she was weak and trusting.

Ó! fuair mise póigín is ní ó chlaidhre, 'S an dara póigín ar
I gat ae kiss whan I cam ben, An ith-er on the

cheann na staighre, An tríú póigín a' gabhail a luí dhom, Is
stair, an' then As I lay doon the best of a', An'

mar-ach an phóg sin do bheinn 'mo mhaighdin: An tríú póigín a'
'twas that kiss brocht my doon-fa': As I lay doon the

gabhail a luí dhom, Is mar-ach an phóg sin ní bheinn gan díd-ean.
best of a', Sin-syne I hae nae roof a va.

Ó! fuair mise póigín, is ní ó chlaidhre,	I gat ae kiss when I cam ben,
'S an dara póigín ar cheann na staighre,	Anither on the stair, an' then
An tríú póigín a' gabhail a luí dhom,	As I lay doon the best of a',
Is marach an phóg sin do bheinn 'mo mhaighdin:	An' 'twas that kiss brocht my doonfa':
An tríú póigín a' gabhail a luí dhom,	As I lay doon the best of a',
Is marach an phóg sin ní bheinn gan dídean.	Sinsyne I hae nae roof ava.
Gheall tú dom, is rinne tú bréag liom,	Ye telt me, but 'twas a' a lee,
Go gcuirfeá fáinne ar mo mhéir dom:	That I your lawfu' bride wad be:
Muileann gaoithe nó sruth dá thréine,	A mill, a burnie plasht wi' rain—
Is beag a neart le h-ais mo phéine:	Their strength is sma' beside my pain:
Muileann gaoithe nó sruth dá thréine,	A mill, a burnie plasht wi' rain
Is luaithe saoghal cailín tréigthe.	Can ne'er mak me a maid again.
Cailín óg mé ar bheagán misnigh,	I'd sit me doon, a tentless lass,
Shiúlfainn an ród le h-óigfhear cliste:	Beside my laddie on the grass:
Níl fíon bán agam, mara n-ólainn uisge,	But drouthie noo I roam the braes,
Agus leanbhín óg agam, is a chóitín briste:	My puir wee bairn in clouted claes:
Níl fíon bán agam, mara n-ólainn uisge,	But drouthie noo I roam the braes,
Ach ocras géar orm, agus tart nár coisgeadh.	Nor breid nor brose my hunger stays.
Cailín óg mé i ngleanntán sléibhe,	I sit and greet upon the knowes,
Ar ghanntan eallaigh is ar bheagán éadaigh,	Nae tocher mine, nae kine, nae yowes,
Is í ar bhreith chloinne is a fear dhá séana,	Dandling a babe whose daddie's gane,
Is nach rí-bhocht an fortún a cheap Mac Dé dhom!	Wi' scorn an' scaith I walk my lane:
Is í ar bhreith chloinne is a fear dhá séana,	Dandling a babe whose daddie's gane,
Ó! is bocht an saoghal do bhochtaibh Dé so!	The puir hae nocht but grief an' pain!

DONAL O'SULLIVAN

1. I got a kiss, and not from a coward, And the second kiss at the head of the stairs, The third kiss as I was about to lie down, And but for that kiss I should be a maid: The third kiss as I was about to lie down, And but for that kiss I should not be shelterless.

2. You promised me, and you played me false, That you would put a gold ring on my finger: A windmill or a stream however strong, Little is their strength compared to my pain: A windmill or a stream however strong, More frenzied is the life of a betrayed girl.

3. I am a young girl of little spirit, Who would walk the road with an active young man: No white wine have I, but water to drink, And a young little baby with his little petticoat broken: No white wine have I, but water to drink, With sharp hunger on me, and a thirst that is unquenched.

4. I am a young girl in a mountain valley, Possessed of no cattle and with little clothing, Bearing a child and repudiated by her man, And how ill is the luck that the Son of God has given me! Bearing a child and repudiated by her man, Oh! 'tis a poor life for God's poor!

IARRAIDH NA nGAMHNA   LOOKING FOR THE CALVES

Andante

Chuir a leas— mham mo lean - abh ag iarr - aidh na ngamhn - a, 'Gus
Her step— moth - er sent her as eve - ning fell To

deamhan ceann a gheódh sí go lá díobh; Cas - adh bar - ún na mbréag dhí _
look _ for the calves that were stray - ing; The bar - on and the rang - er had

ar _____ a' mbeal - ach, Is maor _ na _ coill - e bhí láimh leis.
planned _ it well, At twi - light my lit - tle girl way - lay - ing.

Siúd iad an dís do _ mhill mo _ lean - abh, Is rún ní dhéan - fa mé go
These are the twain that _ ru - ined my child, And let the world _ take _

bráth _____ air, 'S má tá dlí ar bith le fáil ins a'
warn - ing, If there's an - y law at all for both

mbail - e seo _ 'mbím, Buain - fe mis - e ceart a - mach do Mháir - ín!
cot - tage and hall, I _____ shall have jus - tice for my Maur - een!

Chuir a leas-mham mo leanbh ag iarraidh na ngamhna,
  'Gus deamhan ceann a gheódh sí go lá díobh;
Casadh barún na mbréag dhí ar a' mbealach,
  Is maor na coille bhí láimh leis.
Siúd iad an dís do mhill mo leanbh,
  Is rún ní dhéanfa mé go bráth air,
'S má tá dlí ar bith le fáil ins a' mbaile seo a mbím,
  Buainfe mise ceart amach do Mháirín!

Chuaidh barún na mbréag go mall tráthnóna,
  A' siúl na coille go fánach;
Cia casadh dhó-san ar a' mbealach
  Ach mo chailín múinte mánla.
D'fhiafraigh sé dhi-si ciara dhíobh í,
  Nó cia an taobh ó n-a dtáinic sí:
" Ag iarraidh na ngamhna d'fhága mise a' baile,
  Is deamhan ceann is féidir liom 'fháil díobh! "

" Tá sgeachóigín chrom i lúibín na coille,
  Is témid-ne araon go lá ann,
Beidh ceólta na n-éan dhár síor-chur a chodla,
  'Gus gheómoid na gamhna amárach.
Gheobham cion saor ó mhaor na coille,
  Bhéaras féarach go lá dhúinn,
Agus beimíd-ne ár suí ag éirghe an lá márach,
  Agus gheómoid an t-eallach ins a' bhfásach! "

Her step-mother sent her as evening fell
  To look for the calves that were straying;
The baron and the ranger had planned it well,
  At twilight my little girl waylaying.
These are the twain that ruined my child,
  And let the world take warning,
If there's any law at all for both cottage and hall,
  I shall have justice for my Maureen!

So late in the evening the baron stalked
  With stealthy tread through the wildwood,
Till his steps crossed the path my darling walked,
  Wrapt in the innocence of childhood.
He asked her name and whence she came,
  " And what seek you, my fairest? "
" Our calves they have strayed and I'm sore afraid
  That like me they are lost in the forest! "

" On the fringe of the wood there's a blackthorn tree,
  Let's shelter beneath it till morning;
The music of the birds will lull you and me,
  Till at dawn the calves are returning.
The forest-ranger will treat us well,
  And the night will soon be over;
As soon as it has gone, with the rising of the sun
  We'll find the calves in the clover! "

" Bheirim féin mo mhallacht do mhaor na coille,
  Óir a d'fhág sé faoi léan go bráth mé.
Och! mo dhaidí féin go dúch ins a' mbaile,
  Ní fhéadam-sa thiacht i n-a láthair! "
" Éist, a bhruinneal, 's ná bíodh ort-sa brón,
  Is cleas é do rinne do mháithrín:
Seo barr mo dhá láimh dhuit, a ghrá, go
        ndeagh-chumann,
  Mo chéad is mo chúig míle slán leat! "

" 'Tis the forest-ranger has caused my doom,
  My lasting curse be upon him!
My daddy grieves for me at home,
  And now I'll be forced to shun him! "
" Do not fret, dear lass, this grief will pass,
  'Twas your step-mother brought you to danger;
In the shelter of my arms you'll be safe from all
        harms,
  And your daddy will prove your avenger! "

DONAL O'SULLIVAN

1. Her step-mother sent my child to look for the calves, And not one of them could she find until day; She met the dissolute baron on the way, And the forest-ranger was with him. These are the two that ruined my child, And I shall never hush it up, And if there is any law in this place where I live, I shall get justice for my Maureen!

2. The dissolute baron went out late in the evening, Walking through the wood on the prowl; Whom should he meet on the way But my gentle, innocent girl. He asked her who she was And whence she had come: " It was to look for the calves that I left home, And not one of them can I find."

3. "There is a drooping thorn-bush in a corner of the wood, And let us go there together till day; The song of the birds will keep lulling us to sleep, And we shall get the calves to-morrow. We shall have a free supper from the forest-ranger, And he will give us pasturage till day, And we shall be up by daybreak to-morrow, And we shall get the cattle in the pasture."

4. " My curse be on the forest-ranger, For he has left me grief-stricken for ever. Alas! my own daddy sorrowful at home, I never again can face him! " " Hush, girl, and do not fret, This is a trick that your mother has played; Here are the tops of my two hands, love, in token of affection, A hundred, yea, five thousand times, farewell!"

In my verse rendering I have represented the concluding lines as having been spoken by the father. It is right to point out, however, that they were more probably spoken by the baron.

IDIR CHAISEAL AGUS DÚRLAS   ON THE ROAD TO TIPPERARY

Idir Chaiseal agus Dúrlas do chonnaic mé mo rúnach,
  Go h-atuirseach túrtha am choinnibh sa' ród;
Do labhair sí go tláth liom de chómhrá bhinn
    ghrámhar,
  'S do chuir sí róm fáilte agus céad míle póg.

On the road to Tipperary I met with my dearie,
  Exhausted and weary, the tears on her cheek;
She hastened to meet me, with kisses did
    greet me,
  Then shyly and sweetly she ventured to speak.

" Seo litir óm *father* agus beannacht óm mháthair,
  'S tú 'fuireach ins an áit seo, a ógánaigh óig;
Gheó tú míle bó ar bán liom is párdún ón
    mbáinrioghain,
  Agus cead a bheith ar láimh liom a choíche 's
    go deó."

" My father agrees, and my mother you'll please,
  If you'll stay at your ease, lad, with me for
    your bride;
Take our farm and our garden, you'll get the
    Queen's pardon,
  And myself you'll be guarding whatever betide! "

" A chailín beag is áille, más fíor a bhfuil tú 'ráidhte,
  Ní dhéanfainn-se do áthrach ar dhá mhíle bó,
Munab é tá mé páirteach le bliain is trí ráithe
  Leis an níon sin Sheóin Dáibhis i gConntae
    Mhuigheó."

" My fond one, my fairest, of maidens the rarest,
  'Tis you are my dearest, and from you I'd not go,
But I'm pledged this last quarter, though I never
    did court her,
  To John Davis's daughter in the County Mayo! "

" Nach é sin an sgéal cráite, 'dul abhaile domh-sa
    amárach
  Gan fios cé is *father* do mo leanbh beag óg! "
" Mise Domhnall Ó Maoláine nár las riamh le náire,
  Gheó tú ar Shliabh Bán mé nó ar a' gcnoc
    is mó ceó! "

" What ruin and shame at the end of love's dream,
  Not knowing the name I may give to my child! "
" I am Donal Mullanny, that ne'er blushed
    before any,
  I'll be found on Knockany or abroad in the
    wild! "

" Mo chreach is mo dhíth-se nach marbh a
    bhí mé
  Sul ar thachair sa' tslí leat mé, a ógánaigh óig!
Beidh mise faoi dhíoma 'gus bean eile 'luí leat-sa
  Gach maidin chiúin aoibhinn 's mé a' sile na
    ndeór!

" My grief and my ruin, that such passionate wooing
  Should prove my undoing, when I fell through
    your charms!
And now I'm left weeping, my solitude keeping,
  While another lies sleeping each night in
        your arms!

" B'fhearr liom ná Éire nó céad púnta den ór craorac
   Nach bhfeicfinn tú ar aon-chor 's nach
      dtiúrainn duit grá;
'S gur b'é d'aithris tú le do bhéal dom gur
      mhearaigh tú na céadta:
   Nachar chuma dom féin sin ach mo mhealla
      mar chách! "

" How I wish, woe is me! I were single and free!
   When I sat on your knee love bloomed in
      my breast.
You'd boast with a smile you could hundreds
      beguile—
   And I ne'er thought it vile till I fell like the rest! "
                                    DONAL O'SULLIVAN

1. Between Cashel and Thurles I saw my sweetheart, Exhausted and weary, coming towards me on the road. She spoke to me shyly in tones sweet and loving, And gave me a welcome and a hundred thousand kisses.

2. " Here is a letter from my father, and my mother's blessing, If you will remain in this place, young lad. You will get with me a thousand cattle at grass and a pardon from the Queen, With leave to be at my side for ever and always."

3. " O fairest little maid, if what you say is true, I would not marry anyone but you for two thousand cows: Only I am betrothed, this past year and nine months, To John Davis's daughter in the County Mayo."

4. " Sorry my case when I go home to-morrow, Not knowing the father of my little baby." " I am Donal Mullanny who never blushed with shame, You will find me on Slievebawn or on the mistiest hill."

5. " My ruin and my sorrow that I was not dead Before ever you crossed my path, young lad. I shall be grieving while another woman lies with you On each mild, misty morning, weeping bitterly.

6. " I would rather than Ireland, or a hundred pounds in red gold, Never to have seen you and given you love. For you told me with your own lips that you had driven hundreds crazy: I would not mind that, if you had not deceived me like the rest! "

The young man in this song was evidently a rapparee or outlaw, and mention of the Queen's pardon in the second verse perhaps indicates that he lived in the reign of Queen Anne (1702–1714), when the rapparees flourished as a result of the Williamite wars. The reference to John Davis's daughter is explained in a note which my friend the late Dr. Douglas Hyde wrote to me in Irish when I first published a version of the song some years ago. The following is a translation of this oddly improbable piece of folk lore:

" When I was young a tree was often shown me on which Davis used to hang any man he found outside of his own boundary, i.e., any stranger whatever. He had permission to do this from the Government. Near his own house the tree was, on the side of the road. It isn't there now, it was knocked down by a storm when I was young. The Davises were very powerful that time. It wasn't in County Mayo the tree was, but a short way out from Dungar in County Roscommon, about four miles from County Mayo. It is likely that this is the same man as the one in the song. The other man said he would be hanged if he went back. That's the meaning of the saying that he was pledged to John Davis's daughter, i.e., the gallows-tree."

HUMOROUS SONGS

It is sometimes said that the Irish are a witty rather than a humorous people, and if a country's folk songs afford a true reflex of the character of its inhabitants this would appear to be the case. Wit is an intellectual quality and laughs at, rather than with, its victims. Humour, which emanates from the heart, is kindlier and more endearing. The English countryman may be less intelligent than his Irish counterpart, but he has a greater sense of humour. The Irish appreciation of the ludicrous has more affinity with that of the ancient Greeks, as exemplified in the plays of Aristophanes and the Greek Anthology. It can, upon occasion, be downright cruel; and Bernard Shaw was not exceeding dramatic licence when, in *John Bull's Other Island*, he portrays the uproarious merriment caused by the slaughter of Haffigan's pig in a motor accident.

To assess the truth of what has been said from the folk song aspect, we should add to the four songs included in this section three others, which, though found in other sections, are in a general sense humorous: "Owen Cóir", "The Mock Lament" and "O'Rourke's Revel Rout" (pp. 155, 86 and 187). The killing of a cock, the affection of a gouty old man for his pony, the riotous behaviour of a drunken mob, the death (real or supposed) of an objectionable husband—such are the typical subjects for Irish fun. This is not to suggest, of course, that these pieces are not amusing. Undoubtedly they are, but that the humour is of a grim sort seems undeniable.

IS DEAS AN BUACHAILL PÁIDÍN   A HANDSOME LAD IS PAUDEEN

Giocoso

Is deas an buach-aill Páid - ín Lá aon - aigh nó mar - a - ga, 'S ní
A hand-some lad is Paud - een On fair - day or mar - ket - day, He's

deis - e ná lá Már - ta Ar thaobh a bháid - ín iom - ar - tha.
just as nice in spring - time A - board his cur - ragh in the bay.

CHORUS

Ór - ó Mhór, a Mhóir - ín, ___ Ór - ó Mhór, a' dtiuc - faidh tú?
Or - o Mór, O Mór - een, ___ Or - o Mór, now will you come?

Ór - ó Mhór, a Mhóir - ín, A chúil - ín óir, a' dtiuc - faidh tú?
Or - o Mór, O Mór - een, O gold - en - haired one, will you come?

Is deas an buachaill Páidín
  Lá aonaigh nó maraga,
'S ní deise ná lá Márta
  Ar thaobh a bháidín iomartha.

  Oró Mhór, a Mhóirín,
    Oró Mhór, a' dtiucfaidh tú?
  Oró Mhór, a Mhóirín,
    A chúilín óir, a' dtiucfaidh tú?

Adúirt sé is dúirt sé,
  Is dúirt sé go dtiucfadh sé:
A léine bhí gan smúdáil—
  'Sé siúd an ní do chongaibh é.

Adúirt sé 's do gheall sé,
  Is dúirt sé go dtiucfadh sé:
A stocaí bhí gan úra—
  'Sé siúd an ní do chongaibh é.

Adúirt sé 's do gheall sé,
  Is dúirt sé go dtiucfadh sé:
Ach an charraig i mBéal Bóirne
  Do buaileadh ins a' mullach air.

Adúirt sé 's do gheall sé,
  Is dúirt sé go dtiucfadh sé:
'S mara dtí sé an lá gheall sé
  Go mbáitear ins a churach é!

A handsome lad is Paudeen
  On fair-day or market-day;
He's just as nice in spring-time
  Aboard his curragh in the bay.

  Oro Mór, O Moreen,
    Oro Mór, now will you come?
  Oro Mór, O Moreen,
    O golden-haired one, will you come?

He told me and he told me,
  He told me that he'd surely come:
His shirt that wanted ironing—
  'Twas that he said prevented him.

He told me and he promised me,
  He told me that he'd surely come:
His stockings wanted darning—
  'Twas that he said prevented him.

He told me and he promised me,
  He told me that he'd surely come:
But a rock that's on Béal Bóirne
  Came tumbling down atop of him.

He told me and he promised me,
  The lies of him, the lies of him!
And if again he fails me
  I hope his boat capsizes him!

                                        DONAL O'SULLIVAN

1. A handsome lad is Paudeen Upon a fair or market day, But not handsomer than on a March day On the side of his rowing-boat.
   Chorus. Oro Mór, O Moreen, Oro Mór, will you come? Oro Mór, O Moreen, O golden-haired one, will you come?
2. He said and he said, And he said that he would come: But his shirt had not been ironed—And it was that prevented him.
3. He said and he promised, And he said that he would come: But his stockings needed darning(?)—And it was that prevented him.

171

4. He said and he promised, And he said that he would come: But the boulder in Béal Bóirne Was hurled upon the top of him.

5. He said and he promised, And he said that he would come: And if he does not come on the day he promised, May he be drowned in his coracle!

Beal Bóirne (verse 4) is a cliff on the Clare side of Galway Bay, pronounced " Bail Borney ": so presumably the faithless Paudeen lived on the Clare side and his sweetheart on the Galway side.

The chorus, being addressed to a girl, is not particularly appropriate to the words and probably belongs to some older love song. Mór (diminutive Moreen) is a feminine name that has long gone out of use; but as it is frequently met with in proverbs it must be of some antiquity. It is generally Englished Martha, Mary or Agnes.

AMHRÁN NA mBRÉAG — THE SONG OF LIES

Moderato

Is greann-úr an ní seo do chím—se'r na bói-thribh, Eas-
'Twas a com-i-cal sight that I saw by the road-side, An

-cú 'gus píob aic-i 'síor—shein-im cheóil dúinn, An breac lughach sa'
eel with the pipes, and he play-ing a broad-side, The trout with fine

linn—och! ba mhín iad a bhróg-a, Is an bhfeac-úir na caoir-e sa'
shoes in the pool by the heath-er, And the sheep cut-ting turf in this

gheimh-re 'buaint mhón-a? Man-gal-um die der-o, dow der-o,
black win-ter weath-er! Man-gal-um die der-o, dow der-o,

CHORUS

díl-is-é, Bog do chos, croth do chos, téan-am a' rinn-ce liom.
dear is he, Stir your foot, shake your foot, come now and dance with me.

Is greannúr an ní seo do chím-se ar na bóithribh,
Eascú agus píob aici 'síor sheinim cheóil dúinn,
An breac lughach 'sa' linn—och! ba mhín iad a
bhróga,
Is an bhfeacúir na caoire 'sa' gheimhre 'buaint
mhóna?

*Mangalum die dero, dow dero, dílis é,
Bog do chos, croth do chos, téanam a' rinnce
liom.*

Dá bhfeicfeá-sa bricín a' breith coinín i bpoll leis,
Is nead ag an bhfuiseóg i bhféasóg an ghanndail,
Cearc uisge 'crónán 's a' buaint ceóil bhreá as
trompaí,
'Gus madarua ar an dteinteán is an sraoilleán ag
amhastruigh.

Dá bhfeicfeá-sa an fhionnóg ar stuaic a' buaint
biolair,
Is Garrán na mBráthar le n-a chárt a' tomhas mine,
An chearc is an bárdal idir an Spáinneach 's an
Turcaigh,
'Gus giorae agus bríste air ag ól fíona ar bórd
luinge.

Do chonnac-sa sgeacha gan mhaidí gan deilgne,
Dhá mhadarua is iad gan chluasa gan earball,
Teampall ar fuaid gleannta is é a' damhas is ag
eiteallaigh,
Is ní bréagaí mé féinigh ná an té seo do
chreidfeadh mé!

'Twas a comical sight that I saw by the roadside,
An eel with the pipes, and he playing a broadside,
The trout with fine shoes in the pool by the
heather,
And the sheep cutting turf in this black winter
weather!

*Mangalum die dero, dow dero, dear is he,
Stir your foot, shake your foot, come now
and dance with me.*

A troutlet was hauling a rabbit so frisky,
And a lark had her nest in a gander's grey whiskers,
The coot had a jews'-harp on which she was
strumming,
Reynard lay on the hearth, and the cricket was
humming.

A crow in the marsh gathered cress with great
zeal,
And a horse had a quart-pot for measuring meal,
A hen and a drake took a voyage to
Spain,
And a trousered hare drank as he sailed o'er
the main.

I saw a blackthorn tree with never a thorn,
A fox with no ears and no tail, all forlorn,
A church that was dancing and waving its
spires—
If you say you believe me, we're none of us
liars!

DONAL O'SULLIVAN

173

1. This is a comical thing that I see on the roads, An eel with bagpipes playing music for us all the time, The sportive trout in the pool—oh! what fine shoes he has, And did you see the sheep in the winter cutting turf?

Chorus. Mangalum die dero, dow dero, dear is he, Stir your foot, shake your foot, come and dance with me.

2. You should have seen a trout pulling a rabbit into his hole, And the lark having a nest in the gander's beard, A water-hen crooning and making fine music on the jew's-harp, And a fox on the hearth, and the cricket barking.

3. You should have seen the crow on the hummock gathering watercress, And the Friars' Nag (probably a place-name) with its quart-pot measuring meal, The hen and the drake 'twixt Spain and Turkey, And a hare with breeches on drinking wine aboard ship.

4. I saw thorn-trees without branches or prickles, Two foxes without ears or tails, A church dancing and leaping all over the valleys, And I am no greater liar than is the person who [says he] believes me!

Nonsense songs of this type occur in Wales, Brittany, Scotland (both the Highlands and the Lowlands) and England, but they seem to be most abundant in Ireland, being found in all the Irish-speaking districts and occasionally in the English-speaking ones as well. But the Anglo-Irish examples usually show the internal assonance which indicates their Gaelic origin, as in the following :

> I saw Shandon steeple a needle for a tailor to sew,
> And I saw the New Bridge making wigs for the County Mayo.
> I saw Enniskillen distilling strong whiskey in Athy,
> And the Empress of Greece plucking geese in a village close by.

In a scholarly article on the whole theme, my friend the late Miss Anne G. Gilchrist describes the object of such songs as "either a bold essay, in competition with others, in fantastic invention of wonders seen and heard, or the triumphant fulfilment of an imposed task in splendid lying, upon whose success the life or liberty of the singer or his friend, or the hand of a princess depends" (*Journal of the English Folk Dance and Song Society*, IV, 113–121). Incident is piled on incident; but, in contrast to such sublime nonsense as Lear's "They went to sea in a sieve", none of the incidents is developed.

The song here given, and the Anglo-Irish one mentioned above, both belong to competitions in lying. The final line of the latter is

> And no man in this world, I can say, saw more wonders than I!

and this line, being conceivably true, lost the singer the prize. It will be seen from the last line of the Irish song that in this case the singer made no such mistake.

AN PÓNÍ BEAG BUÍ   THE YELLOW PONEE

Allegretto

Tá buach-aill ar mh'eól-as 's is brón liom a shlí, Do
I know a young lad, and I pit-y him too, Who

seól-adh sa' bhfomhar é i dtreó chun Mhi-chíl; Do
set out one eve-ning last aut-umn to woo; He was

geall-adh Peig óg dó le pós-a mar mhnaoi, Dá
prom-ised young Peg-gy his sweet-heart to be, If he

bhfaghadh sé dhá bhó 'gus an pón-í beag buí.
brought her two cows and the Yel-low Pon-ee.

Tá buachaill ar mh'eólas 's is brón liom a shlí,
Do seóladh sa' bhfomhar é i dtreó chun Mhichíl;
Do gealladh Peig óg dó le pósa mar mhnaoi,
Dá bhfaghadh sé dhá bhó 'gus an póní beag buí.

I know a young lad, and I pity him too,
Who set out one evening last autumn to woo;
He was promised young Peggy his sweetheart to be,
If he brought her two cows and the Yellow Ponee.

Nuair imigh an fomhar bhí cead pósta ag an mnaoi
Agus teachtaire seóladh chun seana-Phaidí,
Féachaint an dtúrfadh aon treó uaidh don
          óigfhear chun tís—
Cúbach is Cróinseach is an póní beag buí.

When the autumn was past it was lawful to wed,
So they sent to old Paddy, his father, and said:
" We must settle the fortune, and will you
          agree
To part with two cows and the Yellow Ponee? "

Do fhreagair Paid Mór iad le glórthaibh a chinn:
" Taithneann a sgeól liom 's an óigbhean mar mhnaoi;
Túrfad dhá bhó dhóibh 'gus tigh an Doirín,
Ach ní sgarfainn go deó leis an bpóní beag buí.

Old Paddy spoke out: " Take this answer to Mike—
Young Peggy's the daughter-in-law I would like;
I will give them two cows and the house on the lea,
But I never will part with the Yellow Ponee.

" Eachtra 'neósfad ar mh'óig-each sa' tír,
Gur i Malla do thóg sé mór-chuid cupaí,
I gCorcaigh, i n-Eóchaill is dar ndóigh i dTráilí,
'Gus ó Chúil Cabhair do fógradh mo phóní beag buí.

" Now wait till I tell you the deeds he has done,
The money he's gained and the cups he has won,
In Cork and in Youghal, and sure, in Tralee,
And Coolcower has heard of the Yellow Ponee.

" Ar an gCurrach 'n-a dhéidh sin do dhéin sé
          an gníomh
Nuair a bhuaidh sé ar Whalebone is ar Wait-awhile groí;
Ar Signal is ar Sir Arthur i rás Chonntae an Rí
Do thóg Dávis an Pláta le n-a phóní beag buí.

" At the Curragh he beat every horse in the field,
When Whalebone and Wait-awhile both had to
          yield;
And Signal was two, and Sir Arthur was three,
When Davis was first on his Yellow Ponee.

" Ó Chlinker le léaghadh dhíbh do théarnaigh a shíol,
Ó Mhonarch, ó Eclipse is ón gCaobaigh le maoiamh,
Amethyst tréitheach do b'fhearr laochas is gníomh,
'Gus is í an Paidrín Mare do rug an póní beag buí.

" His pedigree, mind you, is worthy his fame;
There's Clinker, and Caobach (a patriot name),
And Monarch, and Amethyst, Lightning-at-Sea,
And the Paddereen Mare foaled the Yellow Ponee.

" A Mhichíl a chomharsa, a stóraigh 's a mhaoin,
Taithneann do mheón liom, do ghnó is do chrích;
Ach dá dtúrfá Peig óg dó faoi dhó 'gus Caitlín,
Ní sgarfainn go deó leis an bpóní beag buí! "

" So Micky, old friend and dear neighbour of mine,
Though I like your proposal, your terms I decline;
You may offer one daughter, or two, or all three,
But I never will part with the Yellow Ponee! "

Ní maith liom go bráth a cháil do rith síos,
Tá gúta ins gach cnámh leis is fásga dathaighe;
Nuair a thigeann sé anáirde ar an rábaire buí
Tógann é den stáir sin go Spá geal Thráilí.

DIARMUID Ó CRUADHLAOICH

Now I never would say a wrong word of old Pad,
But with gout and rheumatics he's terrible bad,
And next time he climbs up on the Yellow Ponee
He must ride for a cure to the Spa at Tralee.

A. MARTIN FREEMAN

1. There is a lad of my acquaintance for whom I am very sorry, He went in the autumn to call on Michael; He was promised young Peg in marriage If he could get two cows and the little yellow pony.

2. When the autumn had passed she had permission to marry, And a messenger was sent to old Paddy, To see if he would give the young man something to set up house with—Crumple and Dun and the little yellow pony.

3. Big Pad answered them and said: " I like what you tell me of her, she seems a good girl; I will give them two cows and the house at Derreen, But I never will part with the little yellow pony.

4. " I'll tell you of the feats of my young steed in the land, In Mallow he lifted a heap of cups, In Cork, in Youghal, and indeed in Tralee, And my little yellow pony was banished from Coolcower.

5. " At the Curragh after that he achieved a triumph, When he beat ' Whalebone ' and sturdy ' Wait-awhile '; Over ' Signal ' and over ' Sir Arthur ' in the King's County race Davis won the Plate with his little yellow pony.

6. Just to tell you his pedigree, he was descended from ' Clinker,' From ' Monarch,' from ' Eclipse,' and from ' Caobach,' no less, From talented ' Amethyst,' unrivalled for deeds of daring, And it is the Paddereen Mare that foaled the little yellow pony.

7. " Michael, my neighbour and my treasured friend, I like your intention, your business methods and your comfortable homestead; But if you were to give him young Peg twice over, and Kathleen as well, I never would part with the little yellow pony! "

8. I never would wish to take away his character, But he has got gout in every bone and spasms of rheumatism; When he mounts up on the yellow spanker, It must take him without a halt to the bright Spa at Tralee.

The author of this light-hearted ditty (and of numerous others) was Diarmuid Ó Cruadhlaoich (Diarmid Crowley), the tailor of Ballyvourney, near Macroom, County Cork. Though he has been dead many years, there are still people living who remember him.

The match between Paddy's son and Michael's daughter Peg was not seriously intended; and the song was composed in derision of "old Pad" (nicknamed Davis) and his pony, an animal which had the sole merit of ambling slowly enough to enable the gout-ridden gaffer to ride.

Coolcower House, mentioned in verse 4, is less than two miles from Macroom, and the place referred to in the previous verse was a ruined sheiling on Paddy's farm.

Caobach was a racehorse owned by O'Sullivan Beare. The eight others are all duly listed in *Weatherby*, and it is surprising that their names should have been known to the tailor, since most of them flourished long before his time. Whalebone, for example, won the Derby in 1810; Clinker's great steeplechase match against Lord Kennedy's Radical was run in 1826, when he did four miles in eleven minutes and a quarter; and the historic phrase "Eclipse first, the rest nowhere" is said to have been uttered at Epsom by Dennis O'Kelly, the owner of that famous animal, so far back as 1769.

Irish Lass, better known as "the Paddereen Mare", was foaled in 1740, her owner being Mr. Archbold of Eadestown, near Naas, County Kildare. She won a Royal Plate at the Curragh in 1745 and another in 1748, and she became one of the most celebrated racers of her time. In 1757 Goldsmith wrote to his brother-in-law Daniel Hodson at Lishoy, "There has been more money spent in the encouragement of the Paddereen Mare there [i.e., in Ireland] in one season than given in rewards to learned men since the times of Usher."

Goldsmith also mentions (*Citizen of the World*, Letter V) that she had been matched against Black and All Black—Sir Ralph Gore's champion, whose stud name was Othello. This seems to be the race through which Irish Lass got the name of the Paddereen Mare, for it is said that somebody put a rosary (Irish, *paidrín*) round her neck.

176

CEARC AGUS COILEACH — A COCK AND A HEN

Ó!_ cearc ag-us coil-each a d'im-igh le chéil-e, 'S do
A_ cock and a hen ram-bled off with each oth-er, They

shiúl-ad-ar Éir-e gur bris-eadh a gcroí; Do_
trav-elled all Ire-land a-round and a-bout, But_

chai-thead-ar seal-ad i Sli-geach i ngéibh-eann, Gur
when they reached Sli-go they met with some both-er, So they

chuir-ead-ar sgéal-a i gcoinn-e lucht dlí.
sent for the law-yers to get them let out.

Do_ bhí siad ann-sin i lár bar-ra 'gus binns, 'S is_
Be-fore ser-geants and judg-es they took up their sta-tion, But the

duin-e gan chéill_ a chuir ionn-ta sgaol, Gur ag
sher-iff stepped for-ward and gave them a fright, So they

Liam Mhac an Ail-igh a- tá siad ar féar-ach, 'G i- the
flew to Mac-Nall-y's, where they got an ov-a-tion, Eat-ing

mon-óg-a sléi-bhe 's n-a gcodl-a 's a' bhfraoch.
ber-ries all day, with safe roost-ing at night.

Ó! cearc agus coileach a d'imigh le chéile,
  'S do shiúladar Éire gur briseadh a gcroí;
Do chaitheadar sealad i Sligeach i ngéibheann,
  Gur chuireadar sgéala i gcoinne lucht dlí.
Do bhí siad annsin i lár barra 'gus binns,
  'S is duine gan chéill a chuir ionnta sgaol,
Gur ag Liam Mhac an Ailigh atá siad ar féarach,
  'G ithe mónóga sléibhe 's n-a gcodla sa' bhfraoch.

A cock and a hen rambled off with each other,
  They travelled all Ireland around and about,
But when they reached Sligo they met with some bother,
  So they sent for the lawyers to get them let out.
Before serjeants and judges they took up their station,
  But the sheriff stepped forward and gave them a fright,
So they flew to MacNally's where they got an ovation,
  Eating berries all day, with safe roosting at night.

[*Cearc*]

Dá bhfeicfeá mo choileach lá aonach na Sráide,
  'S a ghillín breá rása 'teacht faoi ins a' tslí,
Bhí a bhríste sa' bhfaisean 's a *watch* ar a bhásta,
  A chlaidheamh breá fáisgthe thairis aniar.
Bhí péire spor geal air den airgead bán,
  A hata faoi lása 's a lámhainní buí;
Bhí a bhuataisí daite de leathar na Spáinne,
  A fhuip i n-a láimh is é 'teacht mar an Rí.

[*Coileach*]

Casadh mé isteach go teach Thomáis Uí
    Uada,
  Bhí cearca go leór ann gan coileach ná ál:
Thosaigh mé orm a' pioca thart thímcheall,
  Go dtáinig an neóin gur ghoireas mo sháith.
" Marbhuigh an coileach sin agad, a
    Mháire,
  Is reamhar a chráig is a spruchaille mór."
Tharrainn sí chuici mé is rinne mo mheádhchain;
  Bhí an coisde uilig sásta mo bhruith is mo dhó.

[*Cearc*]

" Mh'och! " ars an chearc is í 'dul ar a' bhfarra,
  " Is brónach 's is deacrach le n-aithris mo sgéal,
Athair mo chloinne 'gus céile mo leaptha
  Bheith 'dul ins a' bpota is leac ar a bhéal!
Tá mé 'mo bhaintrigh a' tíocht ráithe an earraigh,
  Agus gráinne ní phiocfad dá ngabhfa sa' gcré,
'S is buan tá mo mhallacht tráthnóna 's ar maidin
  Do mhnáibh Dhoire Leathain a mharbhuigh
    mo ghéim! "

[*Hen*]

Astride of his racehorse my rooster looked dashing
  Amid the great concourse at market or fair,
A watch at his waist and his breeches in fashion,
  His gleaming sword drawn for his foes to beware.
His spurs were of silver, a sprig of white heather
  Stuck in his laced hat that swept down to each wing,
His shiny boots made of the best Spanish leather,
  A whip in his claw as he strode like a king.

[*Cock*]

At the door of Tom Hood's place I stood awhile
    watching,
  There were hens by the dozen but no cock at all;
I strutted around with my picking and scratching,
  Till divil a hen but would come at my call.
But the housekeeper caught me and tied me and
    weighed me,
  I felt in my gizzard my end had drawn near;
Beside a sharp knife on the table she laid me,
  And that was the finish of poor Chanticleer!

[*Hen*]

" Alas! " said the hen when she heard the sad story,
  " And who is there now to look after my chicks ?
To think of an end so untimely and gory
  For my mate on the roost and the father of six!
I'm husbandless now, what's the use of my laying?
  Not a grain will I pick till I go to the clay;
But I'll spend all the rest of my days in inveighing
  'Gainst the wretches who stole my bold
    game-cock away! "

DONAL O'SULLIVAN

1. A cock and a hen went off together, And they travelled Ireland till their hearts were broken; They spent some time in gaol in Sligo, Till they sent word for the lawyers to come. There they were then with bench and bar around them, And it was a senseless person who gave them a fright, And now they are out on grass at William MacNally's, Eating cranberries and sleeping in the heather.

2. You should have seen my cock on the day of Straide fair, Astride his fine racing gelding in the roadway, His breeches were in fashion and his watch at his waist, His fine sword tucked in behind him. He had a pair of shining spurs made of white silver, A laced hat and yellow gloves; His polished boots were of Spanish leather, A whip in his hand as he progressed like the King.

3. I turned into Thomas Hood's house, There were plenty of hens there, but no cock or brood: I started to pick around and about, Till evening came and I crowed my fill. " Kill that cock of yours, Mary, His claw is fat and his gills are big." She drew me towards her and weighed me; The whole lot of them were content to broil me and roast me.

4. " Alas! " said the hen as she was going to roost, " Sad and tearful is the tale I have to tell: The father of my children and the partner of my bed Going into the pot with the lid on his beak! I am widowed at the coming of the spring quarter, And not a grain of any sown crop will I pick, And lasting is my curse both morning and evening On the women of Derrylahan who killed my game-cock! "

SONGS OF THE HARPERS

The harp is of extreme antiquity in Ireland, and the harper formed an integral part of that Gaelic cultural civilization which had endured for centuries before the consolidation of English dominion under the Tudors. Harpers were held in high esteem as members of the retinue of kings and chieftains, in whose great halls they gave their performances; but the kind of music they played is now unknown. That cultural civilization, menaced by Henry VIII and Elizabeth, was shaken to its foundations under Cromwell and may be said finally to have come to an end over the entire country with the advent of William III and the inauguration of the Penal Laws.

The professional harpers, however, persisted up till the end of the eighteenth century, but their manner of life changed with the changing times. They became itinerants, travelling Ireland on horseback and staying as honoured guests at the Big Houses, where they played their repertoire of Irish airs and occasionally took pupils. They were much in request on special occasions, such as weddings and funerals, and received in return that lavish hospitality for which Ireland has always been famous.

Some of the harpers were composers as well as executants, but very few of their tunes have survived. An exception is provided by Carolan (1670–1738), the latest in date of them all but the greatest in point of celebrity. Upwards of two hundred of his pieces have come down to us, many of them with the verses which he made for them and to which he sang them. For a definitive edition of his music, *see* my *Carolan. The Life Times and Music of an Irish Harper* (two volumes, London: Routledge and Kegan Paul, Ltd., 1958).

MAILÍ SAN SEÓIRSE   MOLLY ST. GEORGE

'Sí'n níon sin San Seóir - se - an — óig - bhean rug barr Le
Miss — Mol - ly — St. — George is — a — maid with - out peer, So —

dei - se, — le — mór - dháil, le sgéimh is le breácht. 'Sí'n —
hand - some, so — mod - est, so grace - ful, so dear. Though de -

ain - near chiúin óg í, 'sí is ionn - raic' a's is fearr Ón —
-mure and re - tir - ing, she — yet far ex - cels The —

tSionn - ainn chun na h-Ó - muí, ón — Ó - muí go Droich - ead Átha, Por -
lass - es of — O - magh, the — dam - sels — of — Kells: From

-tum - na na — long is go — Luim - neach na mbád, Go —
lake - side Por - tum - na to — Lim - er - ick sound, There's no

deimh - in, a Mhail - í mhaigh - dean, níl do leithid - se le fáil!
doubt - ing, — maid — Mol - ly, your like is not found!

'Sí an níon sin San Seóirse
    an óigbhean rug barr
Le deise, le mórdháil,
    le sgéimh is le breácht.
'Sí an ainnear chiúin óg í,
    'sí is ionnraic' a's is fearr
Ón tSionainn chun na h-Ómuí,
    ón Ómuí go Droichead Átha,
Portumna na long is
    go Luimneach na mbád,
Go deimhin, a Mhailí mhaighdean,
    níl do leithid-se le fáil!

Is mé an síogaí ón ndíleann
    ar bhruach loch' a' snámh,
Is mé an síogaí ga mo dhíbirt
    ó Ghaillimh 's gach áit.
Bíonn líon ar gach taobh dhíom
    chuir na mílte chun báis,
Líon a mbíonn síothbhraíocht
    is líon a mbíonn grá:
Mo chreach mór 's mo dhíth nach
    i líon aca táim,
'S gan m'fhuasgailt ag aoinneach
    ach ag an mhaighdean deas mná!

Miss Molly St. George is
    a maid without peer,
So handsome, so modest,
    so graceful, so dear.
Though demure and retiring,
    she yet far excels
The lasses of Omagh,
    the damsels of Kells:
From lake-side Portumna
    to Limerick sound
There's no doubting, maid Molly,
    your like is not found!

I'm a sprite from the deluge,
    afloat on the lake,
A sprite that is banished
    from mountain and brake,
With nets on each side in
    which thousands have strove,
A net full of magic,
    a net full of love.
How I wish that in either
    imprisoned I'd been,
With a hope of release at
    the hand of my queen!

Tá mo cháirde gá shíor-rá liom
    go bhfuilim gan chéill,
Go bhfuil grá agam ar Mháire
    's gan fáth dhomh bheith lé:
Go mbíom gá síor-shása
    's ag innse na mbréag,
'S gur binne liom nó cláirseach
    foghar a béil.
Tá an bás ga mo chrá 's is
    fogus domh an t-éag,
Go deimhin, a Mhailí mhaighdean,
    muna ngéabhair liom féin!

TOMÁS Ó COINDHEALBHÁIN

My friends all keep saying
    I'm foolish and wild,
That in loving maid Molly
    my hopes are beguiled:
When I wish to persuade her
    I tremble, I'm mute,
For her voice is far sweeter
    than viol or lute.
Oh! life is a burden and
    death hovers near,
If you tell me, maid Molly,
    you'll be not my dear!

DONAL O'SULLIVAN

1. Miss St. George is the young lady who bears the palm For comeliness, for grace, for beauty and splendour. Of quiet young maidens she is the noblest and best From the Shannon to Omagh and from Omagh to Drogheda, [From] Portumna of the ships and to Limerick of the boats, Verily, maid Molly, your peer is not found!

2. I am a sprite from the deluge floating on a lake-bank, A sprite that is banished abroad out of Galway, Nets on each side of me that have dealt death to thousands, A net wherein is magic and a net wherein is love. Alack and alas! that I am not in one of those nets, With no one to succour me but this pretty maid!

3. My friends all keep saying to me that I am a fool, That I cherish Mary with a hopeless love, That I am always pleasing her with lying speeches, And that sweeter to me than the harp is the music of her voice. Oh! death is tormenting me and my end is near, Unless, maid Molly, you go with me!

The words and music of this song were composed by Thomas Connellan, a celebrated harper-composer of the late seventeenth century. He was born at Cloonmahon, County Sligo, and is said to have been the composer of upwards of seven hundred airs. Very few of these have survived, though probably a number of them form part of the great body of Irish traditional music without being identifiable as his. According to one tradition, Connellan crossed over to Scotland and was accorded high civic honours in Edinburgh, where he died.

The St. Georges were a family of English origin settled in County Leitrim, its head being Sir Oliver St. George, Bart., of Carrickdrumrusk (Carrick-on-Shannon). The subject of Connellan's song may have been Miss Mary St. George, daughter of Lieutenant-General Richard St. George, Commander of the Forces in Ireland. On the 15th July, 1749 she married James Mansergh, of Macrony Castle, County Cork.

The professional harper-composers were uninfluenced by religious or racial feeling and made songs for the members of the great houses irrespective of whether these were of the old Catholic Gaelic stock or were the Protestant descendants of those who had supplanted them. The poetry was of the courtly type, evincing little depth of emotion; and Connellan's composition for Molly St. George, though in form a love song, lacks any genuine element of passion.

CUPÁN UÍ EAGHRA   O'HARA'S CUP

Risoluto

Dá___ mbeinn-se i n-Ár-ainn nó i gCáir-linn na_ séad, Mar_
Were I ov-er in Ar-an or___ Car-ling-ford shade, Where

ngluais-eann gach sár-long le_ clair-éad 's le_ méad, Ó!___
tall barks of swift-ness bear_ clar-et_ and_ mead, 'Twere_

b'fhearr liom mar shás-amh, is fáim é_ dam féin, Cup-
joy to my_ bos-om in glad-ness to_ sip O'-

-án_ geal Uí_ Eagh-ra,_ 's a_ fháil lán le mo bhéal! Ó!___
-Har-a's_ bright wine-cup_ filled high to my_ lip! 'Twere_

b'fhearr liom mar shás-amh, is_ fáim é_ dam féin, Cup-
joy_ to_ my_ bos-om_ in_ glad-ness to_ sip O'-

-án_ geal Uí Eagh-ra,_ 's a_ fháil lán le mo bhéal!
-Har-a's_ bright wine-cup_ filled high to my_ lip!

Dá mbeinn-se i n-Árainn
  nó i gCáirlinn na séad,
Mar ngluaiseann gach sár-long
  le clairéad is le méad,
Ó! b'fhearr liom mar shásamh
  is fáim é dam féin
Cupán geal Uí Eaghra
  is a fháil lán le mo bhéal!

God é siúd dob áil dam,
  's a liacht ádh maith 'n-a dhéidh?
'Sé deir ollamh na h-áite,
  dar mo láimh-se ní bréag:
A Thrialaigh Bhriain ádhmhail,
  tar tráth fá mo dhéin,
Go n-ólam as an tsár-chupán
  sláinte bhreá Chéin!

TOIRDHEALBHACH Ó CEARBHALLÁIN

Were I over . . Aran
  or Carlingford shade,
Where tall barks of swiftness
  bear claret and mead,
'Twere joy to my bosom
  in gladness to sip
O'Hara's bright wine-cup,
  filled high to my lip!

Why praise what is sought for
  by old man and youth?
While the doctors and sages
  (by this hand I am sooth)
Cry, Turlough, sweet harper,
  come timely to drain
That costly, tall wine-cup
  to the health of brave Kean!

EDWARD WALSH

1. If I were in Aran or in wealthy Carlingford, Where every splendid ship is sailing with claret and mead, I would be better content to obtain for myself The bright cup of O'Hara and to have it full to my lip!

2. Why should I [specially] desire this, seeing that so many good things follow it? And says the sage of the district (by my hand, this is no lie): Turlough, son of fortunate Brian, come join me awhile, That we may drink from the splendid cup a good health to Kean!

Carolan was born in 1670 near Nobber, County Meath. While he was still a child his parents left for Connacht, where his father was successively employed by the St. George family of County Leitrim and the MacDermott Roes of Alderford, County Roscommon. Mrs. MacDermott Roe was attracted to the boy and provided for his education; and when he lost his sight through smallpox she had him taught the harp. He began his career as an itinerant harper at the age of twenty-one and gave early evidence of his genius for composition. For more than forty years he followed his profession, travelling extensively throughout Ireland and making melodies for his patrons and the members of their families. Towards the end of his life he returned to Alderford, where he died on the 25th March, 1738.

This rousing drinking song was composed for Cian Ó h-Eaghra (Kean O'Hara) of Nymphsfield, Collooney, County Sligo. The O'Haras were settled from a remote period in the barony of Leyney in that county, and Carolan's patron (c. 1657–1719) was High Sheriff of Sligo in 1703 and 1713. He married in 1704 Eleanor, the daughter of Theobald Mathew of Thomastown, County Tipperary. Their son, also named Kean (1713–1782), was a Drury Lane playwright of some note in his day, his best known drama being *Midas*.

DR. SEÁN Ó HAIRT   DR. JOHN HART

Moderato

Raghaidh mis - e — suas an uair—— seo gan bhréig, Mar
Now I'll a - rise and straight I'll make my way To

bhfuil sag - art gean— amhail d'uais - libh árd Gaedheal:
see the gent - le priest, the theme of my lay:

Fear breá íog - air tap - aí, Fear lé' sgaoil - tear gas - raí, 'S ar
Vir - tue, strength and vig - our, Kind - ness, pat - ience, rig - our, All

Sheán Ó— hAirt go ceart a labh - raim— féin.
these are— John O' - Hart's, I'm bold to——— say. With

Fear don aic - me sgaip - feadh fíon go réidh, Ag - us
lav - ish hand dis - pens - ing wine so gay, For——

líon - fadh thart go fras do mhac a' cheoil is—— léighinn; Dá—
bard and sage he'd charm— the—— hours a - way; Were

mbeinn sa' Róimh mar b'ait liom, 'S bíodh mo bhót' ion - ghlac - tha,
Car - ol - an (small hope!) To reign in Rome as Pope, A

'S fíor go ndéan - fainn eas - bog mór dhíot féin!
mit - red bish - op sure you'd be this day!

185

Raghaidh mise suas an uair seo gan bhréig,
Mar bhfuil sagart geanamhail d'uaislibh árd Gaedheal:
    Fear breá íogair tapaí,
    Fear lé' sgaoiltear gasraí,
'S ar Sheán Ó h-Airt go ceart a labhraim féin.
Fear don aicme sgaipfeadh fíon go réidh,
Agus líonfadh thart go fras do mhac a' cheóil is léighinn:
    Dá mbeinn sa' Róimh mar b'ait liom,
    'S bíodh mo bhóta íonghlactha,
'S fíor go ndéanfainn easbog mór dhíot féin!

Leigheas do phreab ar aicíd glórthaí a bhéil,
Go mba buan é i bhfad, is clú don Órd é go léir.
    Níl fear, níl bean ná leanbh
    Bheith ar easbhuí teagaisg
Nach ndéanfadh seisean seanmóir mór dóibh le céill.
Stíobhard ceart do Mhac na Glóire é féin,
A' préalóid deas do mhór-fhol' Uí Néill:
    Níl sin uair ná tráth,
    Dá bhfuínn-se uain ar chách,
Nach n-ólfainn suas gan spás a shláinte bhreá shéimh!

         TOIRDHEALBHACH Ó CEARBHALLÁIN

Now I'll arise and straight I'll make my way
To see the gentle priest, the theme of my lay:
    Virtue, strength and vigour,
    Kindness, patience, rigour,
All these are John O'Hart's, I'm bold to say.
With lavish hand dispensing wine so gay,
For bard and sage he'd charm the hours away:
    Were Carolan (small hope!)
    To reign in Rome as Pope,
A mitred bishop sure you'd be this day!

His soothing voice the sick will instant heal,
A model he to guide the Church's weal.
    All who crave instruction
    Glean comfort from his diction,
The mysteries of Faith that he'll reveal.
The way of Christ the Son he treads with zeal,
A princely scion of the great O'Neill;
    There's no occasion now,
    And ne'er will be, I vow,
When I'll not gladly toast a priest so leal!

         DONAL O'SULLIVAN

1. I shall go up straightway without fail To where the lovable priest resides of the noble Gaelic stock: A fine man, keen and alert, A man through whom companies are set free, Truly it is of John O'Hart that I speak: A man of the type that will dispense wine freely, And will make it circle without stint for disciples of music and learning. If I were in Rome as I should like to be, And if my vote were receivable, Verily I would make a bishop of you!

2. The tones of his voice are an instant cure for disease, Long may he flourish, he is a credit to the entire clergy. There is no man, no woman or child In need of instruction To whom he will not deliver a fine homily, full of sense. A true steward is he of the Son of Glory, The splendid prelate of the great blood of O'Neill. There is no hour or occasion, Granted the opportunity, That I will not readily drink his good health!

Carolan's devotion to the faith of his forefathers was deep and abiding, and in this piece he gives touching evidence of the religious zeal of a simple priest at the height of the Penal Laws, when the clergy were proscribed. Dr. John Hart lived at Cloonmahon, County Sligo, and on his mother's side he was of the princely blood of O'Neill, a fact to which the poet alludes. Carolan's wish that he should be made a bishop was fulfilled, for he was appointed to the See of Achonry in 1735, dying four years later. The bishop was renowned for his hospitality and for his kindness to birds, particularly caged birds, which he released wherever possible; and there is a pleasing legend that when he died all the birds of the neighbourhood assembled at the funeral and chanted his requiem. Such was his modesty that he attempted to have this song of Carolan's entirely suppressed—fortunately without success.

The instrumental portion of the tune is found in the original manuscript, and it is likely that it was played by the composer between the verses.

PLÉARÁCA NA RUARCACH   O'ROURKE'S REVEL ROUT

Pléar - ác - a___ na Ruar-cach i gcuimh-ne gach uil - e dhuin-e Dá
O'- Rourke's rev - el___ rout let no per - son for - get___ Who

dtioc - faidh, dá dtáin - ic, 's dá mair - eann go fóill:
has been, who will be, or nev - er was yet. See

Seacht bhfi - chid muc,___ mart ag - us caor - a Dhá
sev - en score hogs in the morn - ing we slay,___ With

gcas - gairt don ghas - raí gach aon ló. Céad
bull - ocks and sheep for the feast - ing each day. Hun - dred

páil uis - ge bhea - tha 's na mead - ra dhá líon - a, Ag
pails us - que - baugh drunk in mud - ders like wort, In the

éir - ighe ar maid - in is ag - ainn bhí 'n spóirt!
morn - ing we rise___ and with us was the sport!

Bris - eadh do phíop - a - sa, slad - adh___ mo___ phóc - a - sa,
My breech - es is stole, my pipe it___ is broke, My

Goid - eadh do bhrís - te - sa, lois - geadh___ mo___ chlóc - a - sa,
pock - et is picked, where the dev - il's___ my___ cloak?___ My

Chaill mé mo bhair - éad,___ m'fhall - aing 'gus m'fhil - éad, Ó
ker - cher I've lost___ and my mant - le's not on, Sev - en

d'im - igh na gair - éad, ar seacht mbeann - acht leó! Cuir
bless - ings be with them, my friends are all gone! Come,

volti

187

spraic ar a' gcláir - sigh, seinn suas a' pléar - ác - a, An
strike up the harp, your mus - ic in haste,— A

buc - sa sin, 'Áin - e, 'gus gread - óg le n-ól!
swill of your li - quor, how qui - et the feast!

Pléaráca na Ruarcach i gcuimhne gach uile dhuine
  Dá dtiocfaidh, dá dtáinic, 's dá maireann go fóill:
Seacht bhfichid muc, mart agus caora
  Dhá gcasgairt don ghasraí gach aon ló.
Céad páil uisge bheatha 's na meadra dhá líona,
  Ag éirghe ar maidin is againn bhí an spóirt.
Briseadh do phíopa-sa, sladadh mo phóca-sa,
Goideadh do bhríste-sa, loisgeadh mo chlóca-sa,
Chaill mé mo bhairéad, m'fhallaing is m'fhiléad,
  Ó d'imigh na gairéad ar seacht mbeannacht leó!
Cuir spraic ar a' gcláirsigh, seinn suas a' pléaráca,
  An bucsa sin, 'Áine, 'gus greadóg le n-ól!

Lucht leanamhna na Ruarcach a' cratha a gcleití,
  Tráth chuala siad tormán nó troimpléasg an cheóil;
D'éirigh gach aon aca gan coisreaca 'n-a leabaidh,
  Is a bhean leis ar strachailt i gach aon chórn.
Nár láidir an seasamh don talamh bhí fútha,
  Gan réaba le sodar agus glug ins gach bróig!
Saol agus sláinte dhuit, 'Mh'leachlainn Uí
    Fhionnagáin!
Dar mo láimh is maith a dhamhsuíos tú,
    'Mhársail Ní Ghriodagáin!
Here's to you, 'mháthair, I pledge you, God save you!
  Beir ar a' sgála so, sgag é in do sgóig.
Craith fúinn an tsráideóg, sín tharuinn an bhán-phluid,
  Tugthar ar sáith dhúinn de lionn-choirm chóir!

A Árd-Rí na gcarad, cébi 'tchífeadh an ghasraí
  Ar líona a gcraicní nó ar lasa san ól!
Cnáimh righe bacaird ar fad in gach sgín aca,
  A' gearra 's a' cosgairt go mór, mór, mór;
A slisneacha darach ar lasa a' gabháil fríd a chéile,
  A' buala, a' greada, a' losga 's a' dódh.
A bhodaigh, 'sé m'athair-se chuir Mainistir na
    Búille suas,
Sligeach is Gaillimh is Caraidh Dhroma Rúisgthe fós.
Iarla Chill' Dara agus Biadhtach Mhuí n-Ealta,
  Siad d'oil agus d'altruim mé, fiosraigh so de Mhór.
Tóig suas a' t'ádhmad agus buail an t-alárm air,
  Preab ionsa táirr agus cic ionsa tóin!

" Cé thóig a' t-alárm so? " ar aon den Eaglais,
  Ag éirghe 'n-a sheasamh 's a' bagairt go mór;
Ní h-é spairgeas uisge coisreactha ghlac sé sa gcíora
  Ach bata maith darach, bog-lán dóirn!
Tráth shíl sé na caithmhílidh a chasgairt 's a chíora,
  Do fágadh an sagart 'n-a mheall chasta fán mbórd.

O'Rourke's revel rout let no person forget
Who has been, who will be, or never was yet.
See seven score hogs in the morning we slay,
With bullocks and sheep for the feasting each day.
Hundred pails usquebaugh drunk in madders like wort,
In the morning we rise, and with us was the sport.
My breeches is stole, my pipe it is broke,
My pocket is picked, where the devil's my cloak?
My kercher I've lost and my mantle's not on,
Seven blessings be with them, my friends are all gone.
Come, strike up the harp, your music in haste,
A swill of your liquor, how quiet the feast!

A-shaking their feathers, just roused from their
    slumber,
By the noise of the harp and of feet without number,
The sons of O'Rourke bounced up in a throng,
Each man with his woman and danced to the song:
Till the ground shaking under partook of their cogues,
Which as they quick trotted glig-glugged in their
    brogues.
Long life and good health to you, Loughlin O'Enegan,
By my hand, you dance bravely, Margery Grinigan!
Here's to you, dear mother, I thank you, dear Pat,
Pitch this down your throat, I'm the better of that.
Come shake us down rushes, an excellent bed,
And over us next the winnow-cloth spread.

Dear Anna, some snuff, to keep me awake,
And a little to drink as long as I speak.
Good heaven, how strange! What must people think?
After filling their skins thus to fight in their drink!
Such stabbing, such gashing, such tugging and
    strife,
Half an arm at least the length of each knife!
What whacking and cracking, with cleftings of oak,
What sounding, rebounding, a hundred heads broke!
My father he built the monastery of Lusk,
With Boyle, Sligo, Galway and Carrickdrumrusk.
Betagh of Moynalty and the Earl of Kildare,
I was nursed by their mother—ask that woman there!

" Who raised this alarm? " says one of the clergy,
A-threatening severely, " Cease fighting, I charge ye! "
A good knotted staff, the full of his hand,
Instead of the spiridis backed his command.
So falling to thresh fast as he was able,
A trip and a box fetched him under the table.

188

D'éirigh na bráithre a' tárrtháil na bruíne,
Is fágadh an t-Athair Gáirdian ar a thárr
'n-áirde sa ngríosaí.
" Tráth bhínn-se ag an bPápa ar stuidéar na ngrásta,
'S a' glaca na ngrádhamh tháll ins a' Róimh,
'Sé an *Seven Wise Masters* bhí agad ar do tháirr,
Is tú a' rósta na bprátaí láimh leis a' tSídh Mhór! "
AODH MAC GABHRÁIN

Then rose a big friar to settle them straight,
But the back of the fire was quickly his fate!
From whence he cried out, " Do ye thus treat
your pastors?
Ye, who scarcely were bred to the Seven Wise Masters!
That when with the Pope I was getting my lore,
Ye were roasting potatoes not far from Sheemore! "
CHARLES WILSON

1. The O'Rourkes' feast is remembered by everybody Who shall come, who is gone, or who is still living : Seven score pigs, beeves and sheep Being slaughtered for the company every single day. A hundred pails of whiskey and the churns being filled, When we rose in the morning 'tis we had the sport. Your pipe was broken, my pocket was picked, Your breeches were stolen, my cloak was burnt, I lost my hat, my mantle and my kerchief, Since the garters(?) have gone, our seven blessings go with them. Strike up the harp, play up the dance, That [snuff-]box, Annie, and a morning appetiser to drink !

2. The O'Rourkes' followers were shaking their feathers When they heard the rumble and clatter of the music; Every man of them got out of bed without blessing himself, With his woman being dragged after every drink(?). Didn't the ground hold out well under them, Not to split through the trampling and gurgling in every shoe ! Health and long life to you, Myles Finnigan ! By my hand, you dance well, Marcella Gridigan ! Here's to you, mother, I pledge you, God save you ! Take hold of this bowl, drain it down your gullet. Shake down that bed for us, stretch the white blanket over us, Let our fill be given us of honest ale !

3. Great heavens ! you should have seen the company When their skins had been filled and they were maddened with drink ! A cubit's length by rule in each of their knives, Slashing and stabbing amain ; Their flaming oaken cudgels belabouring each other, Beating, roasting, scorching and burning. You churl, it was my father built Boyle, Sligo, Galway and Carrick-on-Shannon too. The Earl of Kildare and the Hospitaller of Moynalty Nursed me and fostered me—ask this of Mór (a woman's name). Take up that board and strike the alarm on it. A blow on the belly and a kick on the bottom !

4. " Who raised this alarm? " said one of the clergy, Rising up and threatening severely. It wasn't the holy water brush he took to assail them, But a stout stick of oak, nearly as thick as his fist ! When he thought to belabour and harass the warriors, The priest was left in a twisted heap under the table. The friars got up to rescue him from the mêlée, And the Father Guardian was left on his belly atop of the embers. " While I was with the Pope pursuing sacred studies, And taking orders yonder in Rome, It was the *Seven Wise Masters* you had on your belly While you were roasting potatoes beside Sheemore ! ".

So far is as known, this is the only case in which Carolan composed an air for the words of another. The author was his contemporary Aodh Mac Gabhráin (Hugh MacGauran), a humorous poet of County Leitrim.

The song embodies the tradition of the Christmas festivities held in the Great Hall of his Castle at Dromahaire by the famous sixteenth century chieftain Brian O'Rourke, Prince of Bréifne, commonly known as *Brian na Múrtha* ("Brian, Razer of Ramparts"). He waged incessant warfare against the forces of Elizabeth and he gave succour to the Spaniards stranded on the west coast after the wreck of the Armada in 1588. Three years later he crossed over to Scotland to seek aid from James VI. But James delivered him to the English —it is said for money—and he was put on trial for treason in Westminster Hall. O'Rourke, whom Sidney described as the proudest man he ever dealt with, understood no English and refused to recognize the court. When told that the indictment was sufficient if he declined to plead, "If it must be so," he replied, "let it be so!" He was accordingly condemned and hanged at Tyburn, his body being afterwards drawn and quartered.

Dean Swift was attracted to the poem and translated the first three verses of it in 1720, the final verse being done by Sir Walter Scott for his edition of Swift's works. Various traditions have it that Swift was assisted by Magauran and Carolan respectively. His rendering is in quatrains :

189

O'Rourk's noble fare
Will ne'er be forgot
By those who were there
Or those who were not,

and so on, and each quatrain should properly translate two lines of the original, giving six quatrains to each verse. Unfortunately, however, Swift takes seven quatrains to translate verse 1, the same for verse 2, and eight for verse 3. For this reason, and also because it is rather more literal, I have preferred to give here the translation made by Charles Wilson and published by him in his *Select Irish Pòems* (1782).

Nothing in the song itself calls for comment, except perhaps the references in the concluding lines of the last verse. Sheemore is a hill in County Leitrim, and the *Seven Wise Masters* was a collection of romances which enjoyed a wide circulation in mediaeval Europe. The friar's point is that while he was acquiring learning in Rome his rustic assailant was occupying himself with frivolous literature.

INDEX OF IRISH TITLES

COMBINED INDEX OF ENGLISH TITLES
AND LIST OF SOURCES

MOCK LAMENT. Tune and text: *Journal of the Irish Folk Song Society*, XIX, 21, noted in 1921 by Wilfrid Brown from the singing of Pádraig Ó Siocfhradha, who learnt the song in 1903 from Seán Ó Conchubhair, Ballymore, Dingle, County Kerry.
page 86

MOLLY ST. GEORGE. Tune and text: my *Bunting Collection*, I, 43. Tune noted by Bunting from Hugh Higgins, harper, of County Mayo; text noted by Patrick Lynch from Denis Hempson, harper, of County Derry. The tune has been modified to bring it within the compass of the voice.
page 181

MOWER, THE. Tune: Petrie MS., no. 1868 (*Stanford-Petrie*, 1206). Text: Dinneen's *Amhráin Eoghain Ruaidh Uí Shúilleabháin* (1907), 12, collated with Ó Donnchadha's *Guth na mBárd* (1914), 34 and Ó Foghludha's *Eoghan Ruadh Ó Súilleabháin* (1937), 40. In lines 1 and 2 of verse 7, I am indebted to the late Professor Gerard Murphy for two emendations which improve the assonance.
page 134

O'HARA'S CUP. Tune: *Joyce* (1909), 342, from the Forde MSS., taken partly from John Windele and partly from Patrick Carey, both of Cork. Text and translation: Walsh's *Irish Popular Songs* (1847), 70, 71. In verse 1, line 1, I have substituted the place-name given in one of the Bunting MSS., with a consequential alteration in the translation. Verse 2, line 1 is hypermetrical and has been amended.
page 183

OLD MAN, THE. Tune: *Journal of the Folk Song Society*, VI, 104, noted by A. Martin Freeman in 1914 from Miss Peg O'Donoghue, Ballymakeery, County Cork. Text: verses 1, 4, 5, 6 and chorus, *ibid.*; verses 2 and 3, *An Claidheamh Soluis*, 3rd January, 1903, 718.
page 75

OLD MAN OF KILCOCKAN, THE. Tune and text: *Journal of the Folk Song Society*, VI, 286–9, noted by A. Martin Freeman in 1914 from Mrs. Mary Sweeny, Coolae, Ballyvourney, County Cork (8 verses).
page 73

ON THE ROAD TO TIPPERARY. Tune: *Journal of the Irish Folk Song Society*, XX, 51, noted in 1923 by Wilfrid Brown from the singing of Pádraig Ó Siocfhradha. Text: verses 1 and 4, *ibid.*, with readings from *An Lóchrann*, January, 1918, 3; verses 2, 3, 5 and 6, my *Bunting Collection*, III, 1. The version in the *Journal*, supplied by Dr. Douglas Hyde, was noted in Philadelphia from a native of Lettermacaward, County Donegal; that in *An Lóchrann* was noted by Fionán Mac Coluim in Valentia, County Kerry; and that in *Bunting* was obtained in County Mayo. The composite version here published, while indicating the wide distribution of the song, involves a certain mixture of dialects which I have been unable to avoid.
page 166

O'ROURKE'S REVEL ROUT. Tune: *Bunting* (1809), 7. Text: my *Bunting Collection*, IV, 24–5. Translation: Charles Wilson's *Select Irish Poems* (1782), 69–72.
page 187

O SOUTH WIND! Tune and text: my *Bunting Collection*, V, 29–30. Text noted by Patrick Lynch from Joseph Rush, shoemaker, Castlebar, County Mayo.
page 95

OWEN CÓIR. Tune: Hudson MSS., I, 424, reproduced in *Journal of the Irish Folk Song Society*, XIII, 12. Text: Hardiman's edition of O'Flaherty's *Iar-Connaught* (1846), 292, collated with Timony's *Abhráin Ghaedhilge an Iarthair* (1906), 71. Translation: Francis A. Fahy's *Irish Songs and Poems* (1887), 37. An imperfect version in *Béaloideas*, X, p. 242 (1940) has interesting notes on the subject of the song.
page 155

O WOMAN WASHING BY THE RIVER. Tune: Petrie MS., no. 717 (*Stanford-Petrie*, 1532). Text: *Petrie* (1855), 74. Tune and text from Mary Madden, a blind ballad-singer of Limerick City, later resident in Dublin. Translation: Sigerson's *Bards of the Gael and Gall* (1897), 344. *page 18*

PALATINE'S DAUGHTER, THE. Tune: *Journal of the Irish Folk Song Society*, XVIII, 24, noted by me in 1921 from the singing of Colm Ó Lochlainn, Dublin. Irish and English texts: *An Lóchrann*, February, 1908, 3, noted by Fionán Mac Coluim from Seán Ó Súilleabháin, Lios Bán, Iveragh, County Kerry.
page 68

PLOUGHMEN'S LILT. Tune: Petrie MS., no. 967 (*Stanford-Petrie*, 1055), with readings from *Petrie* (1855), 30. Text: *Petrie* (1855), 30. Tune and text from Teigue MacMahon, a blind countryman of County Clare.
page 37

PRECIOUS TREASURE, THE. Tune: *Petrie* (1882), 35, from Frank Keane. Text: *ibid.*, from Eugene O'Curry, with a few readings from *Journal of the Irish Folk Song Society*, XXI, 44. Verse 1, line 9, seems defective and has been amended.
page 34

PULSE OF MY HEART. Tune: *Petrie* (1855), 55, noted by William Forde in Connacht. Text and translation: Walsh's *Irish Popular Songs* (1847), 142.
page 63

RACES OF BALLYHOOLY, THE. Tune: *Joyce* (1909), 4, from Joyce's childhood memory. Text: *Gaelic Journal*, XIII (1903), 212 (7 verses), with a reading from *Éigse*, II, 92.
page 157

RED-HAIRED MAN'S WIFE, THE. Tune: Petrie MS., no. 846 (*Stanford-Petrie*, 1300), "A cos deas i mbróg". Text and translation: Hyde's *Love Songs of Connacht* (1893), 92–95.
page 47

REPENTANCE OF JOHN HOARE, THE. Tune: my *Bunting Collection*, VI, 85, amended from the MS. copy: "Domhnall Meirgeach". Bunting's original, noted by him from Mrs. Burke, Carrowkeel, County Mayo in 1792, is reproduced at p.82. Text: O'Daly's *Irish Language Miscellany* (1876), 32, collated with R.I.A. MS. 23 C 26 (11 verses).
page 103

SMALL BLACK ROSE, THE. Tune: Walsh's *Ár gCeól Féinig* (1920), 12. Text: Walsh's *Irish Popular Songs* (1847), 56, collated with O'Daly's *Poets and Poetry of Munster*, First Series (1849), 210 (6 verses at former reference).
page 132

SNOWY-BREASTED PEARL, THE. Tune, text and translation: *Petrie* (1855), 10, 11. Tune and text from Eugene O'Curry. Dr. Petrie's verse translation of this beautiful song is justly celebrated, but it is not in the strict metre of the original. It can, however, be sung to the tune with but slight modification of the latter. *page 46*

INDEX OF FIRST LINES

IRISH

INDEX OF FIRST LINES

ENGLISH

197

INDEX OF POETS

INDEX OF TRANSLATORS